a number of things

Practical and creative ideas for the development of number skills
with children from four to seven years

Kathie Barrs and Sue Logan

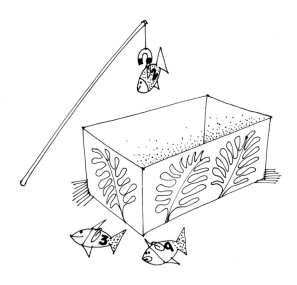

Line drawings by Tony Barrs

First Published in 1997 by
BELAIR PUBLICATIONS LIMITED
P.O. Box 12, Twickenham, England, TW1 2QL

© 1997 Kathie Barrs and Sue Logan
Series Editor Robyn Gordon
Designed by Lynn Hooker
Photography by Kelvin Freeman
Typesetting by Belair
Printed in Hong Kong through World Print Ltd
ISBN 0 947882 64 2

Acknowledgements

The authors and publishers would like to thank the children of Great Bardfield Primary School, Braintree, Essex, for their contributions in the preparation of classroom displays.

The authors would also like to thank Helen Jolly for her help and support, and Shirley Stewart for her inspiration.

Games made by older children for younger children - see page 35

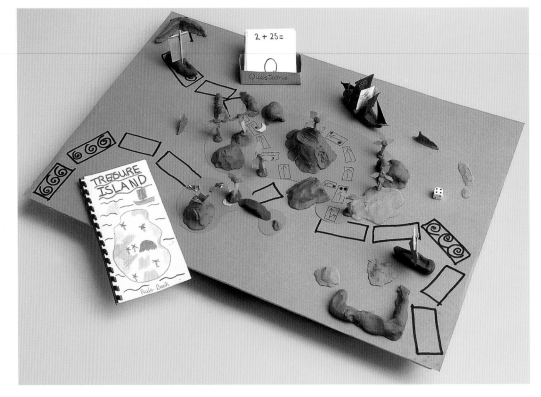

Contents

Introduction

Our aim in writing *A Number of Things* is to provide inspiring and thought-provoking activities for number work in the infant classroom. During the early stages, some concepts and skills need repetition, and a fresh approach is often needed in order to maintain interest and enthusiasm.

The book is organised in two main sections, the first dealing with the development of skills and the second with the teaching of number through popular infant topics. Opportunities for handling larger numbers are provided through practical activities involving measuring.

Throughout the book, we have suggested games to reinforce the skills introduced, and have also included ideas for interactive, three-dimensional displays.

We have attempted to promote an investigative, open-ended approach wherever possible. By providing a stimulating atmosphere where children can challenge and question, they will develop a thorough understanding of number, and a fascination which will last much longer than their infant years.

Kathie Barrs and Sue Logan

NUMBERS 0 - 10

One-to-one matching - formation and recognition

Get the children to make counting apparatus from clay with the help of parents or older children

• Use items in the environment which require matching, for example, egg to eggcup, knife to spoon, cup to saucer, in order to give sorting activities a purpose. Make use of situations where the children are getting dressed to talk to them about matching buttons to button holes, fingers to gloves, etc.

Play "Zoo", which gives practice in counting, 1 - 1 matching, recognising numbers to 10, and number-to-word matching.
For two players, you will need:
    2 game boards, covered with gift wrapping paper (patterned with animals)
    A set of cards made from the same paper

To play:
Each child takes a playing board. The cards are placed face down in a pile, and players take turns to turn over the top card. If it matches an animal on their board, they take it and place it on top of the matching animal. If they do not have a match, the card is returned to the bottom of the pile. The winner is the first one to complete his/her board.

- Traditional activities, such as making, for example, "My Book About 5", are an essential experience at this stage.
- Make and play simple games which require the children to match the appropriate number of items to the written symbol.
- Have a "Number of the Day", where a group of children has the responsibility to each bring to school a collection of, for example, five objects to display. On a "5" day, you could also practise writing that number, getting into groups of that size, clapping five times, painting a picture of five items, etc.

- **Use "colour by number" pictures** to help the children to distinguish between numbers and other kinds of writing. Ask them to colour the shapes which have a number written on them, and to leave blank the shapes which have a different kind of writing on them.

Play "Mary Mary, Quite Contrary".
For up to four players, you will need:
    4 base boards
    1 die.

To play:
Each player has a base board and counters. Players take turns to throw the dice, say the number out loud and then check the 'key' to see which flower they can cover. The first player to cover all the flowers is the winner. If a player throws a number and all the flowers relating to that number are covered, s/he misses that turn.

- Make string numbers. Draw a number on a piece of card, and then measure and cut lengths of string or wool and lay over the number. Repeat for all the numbers to 10. Find which number needs the longest piece of string. Do any numbers need more than one piece? Glue the string down and display.

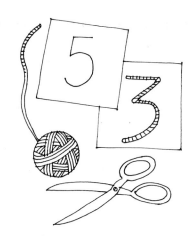

Counting, estimation and number lines

- Get the children to sit in a circle and let them count round up to 10. As soon as they reach 10, they should start again at 1. Develop this by making it harder as they improve, perhaps with only every other child saying the numbers, or the children wearing black shoes, etc.

Use well-known songs and nursery rhymes to make 2D and 3D number lines. Whilst singing the song, the children can use the display to show the numbers.

- Ensure that the children get plenty of practice in counting on from a given number rather than always from 'one'. For example, give 10 children a card each with a number between 1 and 10 written on it and ask them to stand in a line in the correct order. Call out a number, and the children holding the next two number cards have to shout out their number in order. For example, if you call out "3!", the ones holding 4 and 5 will shout out "4!" and "5!".

- Make a series of cards with pictures of ladybirds on them. Cover these with adhesive plastic, and ask the children to complete the patterns of dots using a chinagraph pencil, so that they can be cleaned off and the card re-used. Other ideas could include leaves on stems, petals on flowers, threads on spiders' webs, etc.

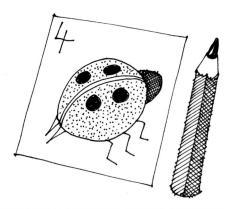

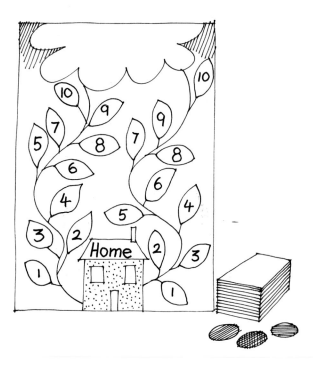

Play "Jack and the Beanstalk".
For two players you will need:
    1 base board
    1 marker for each player
    a set of cards marked:

Go on 1 (x 3)	Go back 1 (x 3)
Go on 2 (x 5)	Go back 2 (x 2)
Go on 3 (x 6)	Go back 3 (x 3)
Go on 4 (x 4)	Go back 4 (x 1)
Sit and rest (x 2)	

To play: Place the cards face down in a pile. Players start with their markers on HOME, and take turns to turn over a card and move their marker accordingly. Should the cards run out, turn the pack over and go through them again. The winner is the first to get to the top of the beanstalk.

Play "Hickory Dickory".
For two players you will need:
    I baseboard
    2 mouse counters
    a spinner or die marked 0,0,1,1,2,2

To play:
The players place their mice at the foot of the clock. They take turns to throw the dice or spin the spinner, and move up the clock by the corresponding number of spaces. Each player must then say the time on the clock s/he has landed on. The first one home is the winner.

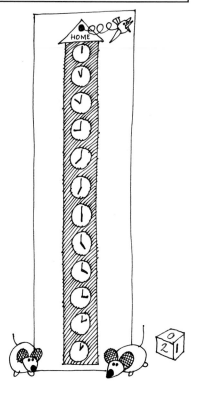

- Paint a giant with a long coat and use the buttons as a vertical number line **(see photograph left)**.

Paint a 'Hickory, Dickory Dock' clock, and attach the mouse using Velcro **(see photograph right)**.

Other ideas for number lines could include "1 potato, 2 potato", "Mary, Mary", "Five Currant Buns".

Dot patterns and conservation

- **Make "Number People".** Allocate a different number to each group of children, and get them to paint a life-sized person wearing as many items as possible which relate to the given number **(see photograph)**.

This could be extended to designing and painting monsters with six eyes, six ears, six fingers, six feet, etc., or to designing an individual item of clothing such as a jumper, where everyone in the group contributes a row with a pattern of 6 on it.

- Play "The Story of....". Investigate the story of a number by finding lots of ways to arrange that particular number of counters on a small sheet of paper. Include 'regular' (for example, three in a triangular shape) and 'random' patterning. Give each child a turn, and then ask them to go and make their own arrangement and colour circles to show the positions of their counters. Talk about this with the children to ensure that they understand that each different pattern comprises the same number of counters. This can also be done using pegboards, asking the children to arrange a given number of pegs in their own way.

- Make a goldfish tank from a board covered in blue paper and decorated with weeds. Cover it with adhesive plastic. Cut out a number of goldfish, stick them on to the tank with adhesive putty and get the children to re-arrange the fish every day. Change the number of goldfish every week.

- Set each group a challenge to make a mobile using a given number of items. Suspend a cut-out number under each mobile.

- Give a group of children X multilink. What arrangements can they make? Now give them the same number of Lego pieces. What arrangements can they make now?

More/less

- A good way to introduce this aspect of maths is to use the children themselves, in groups no larger than ten. Ask how many have black hair, blue socks, etc., and introduce the concept and language of *more* and *less*. The children could then choose one aspect and paint the result. This work could lead on to constructing simple graphs and pictograms based, for example, on the weather. It is useful to include a category that you know won't be filled at all, such as snow in the summer, in order for the concept of 0 to be discussed.

Play "Grabba".
For any number of players, you will need:
      a pile of cards with numbers from 0 to 10
      Multilink cubes

To play:
Place the cards face down in the middle of the table, next to a pile of Multilink. The players take turns to pick up a handful of cubes, and then turn over a card. Each has to say whether the number of Multilink s/he has taken is more or less than the number on the card. If correct the player can keep the card. The winner is the player with the most cards at the end of the game. To make this game self-correcting, dots as well as the number can be written on the card, and after their prediction of more or less, the child can place cubes on the dots to check.

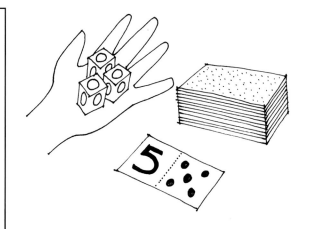

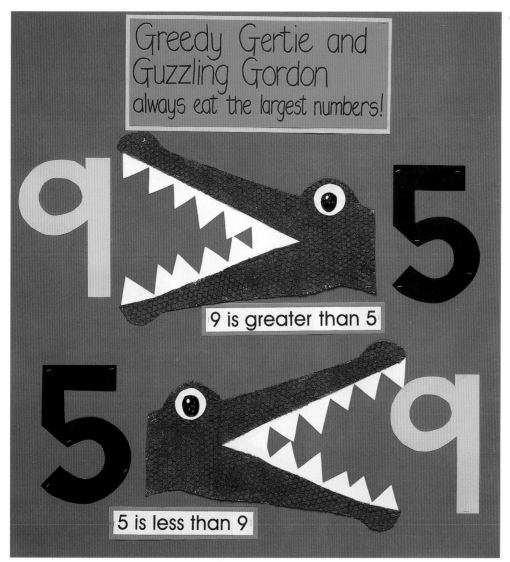

Greedy Gertie and Guzzling Gordon always eat the largest numbers!

9 is greater than 5

5 is less than 9

- **To introduce the symbols < and > use the idea of a greedy crocodile** who always wants to eat the largest number. Because of this, his open mouth points towards the largest number, ready to gobble it up!

The children can make their own individual greedy crocodile mouths using paper fasteners.

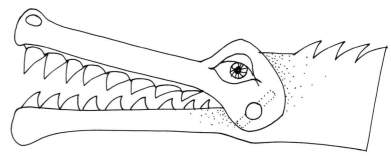

Play "More or Less?".

For any number of players you will need:

      a set of cards with three each of the numbers from 1 to 9

      a set of cards, half with "More" and half with "Less" written on them

      counters

To play:

Place the two sets of cards face down in the centre of the table. The players take turns to turn over a number card, and then a "more/less" card. S/he then has to say a number which is more or less, depending on the card turned over. If correct, that person collects a counter. The cards are returned to the bottom of the appropriate piles. The winner is the player with the most counters after an arranged number of turns.

Ordering and ordinal numbers

- At the beginning of a new school year, give every child in the class a number according to their position in the register. This will, of course, entail numbers larger than 10, but is a very useful activity for many different organisational reasons - for lining up, for dividing the class in half or quarters, for teaching odd and even numbers, counting in 2s, etc. The children find it fun, and quickly come to recognise larger numbers.

- Don't forget to line the children up occasionally in reverse order! Use every opportunity when the children are lining up to point out who is in front of whom, and who is behind.

- Give the children large cards with numbers 0 - 10, and get them to order themselves. Try removing some numbers - can they still put themselves in order? **Make number hats instead of pieces of card (see photographs).**

- Draw simple mazes and get the children to find their way out by following the numbers from 1 to 10 in the correct order. Extend this by using mazes with the numbers written in reverse order.

- Pick a series of small flowers, such as daisies, making sure that all the stems are of different lengths. Press them, stick them on to identical pieces of card and cover with adhesive plastic. Write a number on the back of each card, starting with 1 for the smallest flower and going to 10 for the largest flower. Make up games to play with these cards, for example:

Play "The Flower Game"
Version 1.

Deal the cards, flower side down, between two players. The players then sort their cards into order by looking at the numbers, for example, 2, 5, 6, 8, 9. This provides an opportunity for the children to order numbers which may not be sequential, and may not start at 1. The game is self-correcting, as the children then turn over their cards to check that the daisies are in size order.

Version 2.

Deal the cards flower-side down. The player with the card with the number 1 on it places it in the centre of the table. The other players take turns to place the next card until all the cards are in a pile in the correct order. Again, turn over the cards to check that the daisies are in size order.

Play "1,2,3,4,5 - The Fishing Game".
For 3 players, you will need:
    3 rods with magnets attached on the end of the line
    a "tank" (a shoe box would be fine)
    3 sets of cardboard fish, each with a number from 0 to 10 on the back, and a paperclip attached to the end of each.

To play:
The fish are placed in the tank, and the children use their magnetic rods to catch them. If they catch a number they already have, they must throw it back. The first to get all their numbers from 0 to 10 is the winner.

- Ask each child in the group to make a stick of four different coloured Multilink cubes. Discuss which colours are 1st, 2nd, 3rd and 4th. Record these on squared paper. Then make a rule, for example: "Swap over the 1st and 3rd". Each child does this, discusses the results using relevant language (1st, 2nd, etc.) and records the colours/numbers of the new stick.

Make a shoe box train with a selection of interesting items in the carriages to promote language and discussion

- Get the children to make up a sentence using four or five words. Write the sentence down, and give each word a number - 1st, 2nd, etc. Now cut up the sentence and ask a child to reassemble the sentence in an incorrect order and then read it back. Is it possible to make a sensible sentence in more than one way? This activity can be extended by talking about the fact that the first word in a sentence has a capital letter, and that the last word is followed by a full stop.

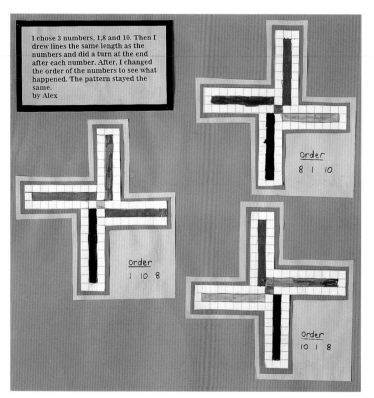

I chose 3 numbers, 1,8 and 10. Then I drew lines the same length as the numbers and did a turn at the end after each number. After, I changed the order of the numbers to see what happened. The pattern stayed the same.
by Alex

- Spiral patterns
Make patterns by choosing three numbers, for example, 1, 2 and 5, and then drawing lines of corresponding lengths on squared paper, turning a corner in the same direction, i.e. right or left, each time.
Then ask the children to change the order of the three numbers to see whether the pattern is different.

How many times can the order of three numbers be changed?

(See photograph to left, and on facing page)

Partitioning

Addition is an activity where two sets are combined to make a third. Care should be taken not to introduce the symbols for addition and subtraction too soon. Allow the children plenty of experience in separating and combining sets and counting the outcomes. Use partitioning and finding the differences in order to introduce the concept of subtraction, and use the term 'subtract' rather than 'take away'. When using interlocking cubes to demonstrate addition, make sure that the two lengths which are to be joined, for example 2 + 3, are of different colours so that the children can still see the '2' and the '3' once they have been combined to make a '5'.

To make the handling of concrete materials easier and less confusing in the early stages, provide the children with apparatus which can be partitioned easily without any bits being lost.

Ideas for this could include cubes in a small, sealed plastic bag, or buttons or beads threaded on a lace. The children can then partition their allocated number of objects and see clearly how many are in each part, and how many there are when the two parts are combined.

Recording can be done in a variety of ways.

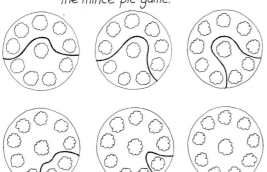

The mince pie game.

Play "The Mince Pie Game".
For four players you will need:

> 6 paper plates with 10 mince pies drawn on each plate. Cut each plate into two pieces, so that you have the following number of mince pies on each piece of plate:
>> 0 and 10
>> 1 and 9
>> 2 and 8
>> 3 and 7
>> 4 and 6
>> 5 and 5
>
> a large book each to use as a screen

To play:
Deal out the pieces of plates. Each player stands the book up to act as a screen so that none of the other players can see his/her pieces. All players then try to match up their pieces to make a complete plate - put to one side as completed. The first player chooses any of the others, and asks "Have you got a piece of plate with X pies on it?" If that child has, s/he must give it up (only pieces which are unmatched should be given away). The first child uses it to make a completed plate, and then has another turn. If the second child does not have the piece asked for, play is resumed. The game continues until all pieces are matched. The winner is the player with the most completed plates at the end of the game.

• **Partitioning Cards**
Use pictures cut from wrapping paper, magazines, stickers, etc., to make attractive cards with objects ranging from 2 to 10. Attach a lace at the top and ask the children to find as many ways as they can to partition the objects into two sets. They can then record this to ensure that they have found all possible sums. Can they find a pattern in the sums? Extend this by using more laces.

(See photographs to left and on facing page.)

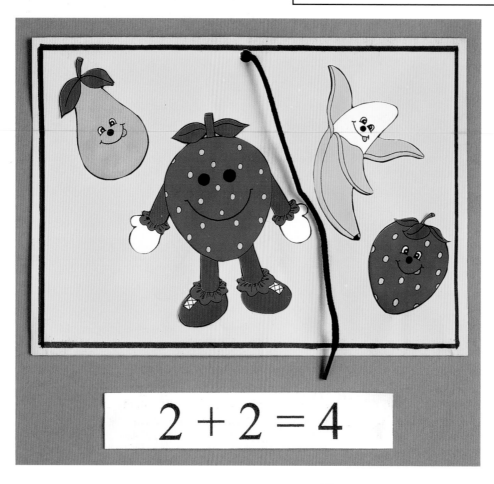

$2 + 2 = 4$

16

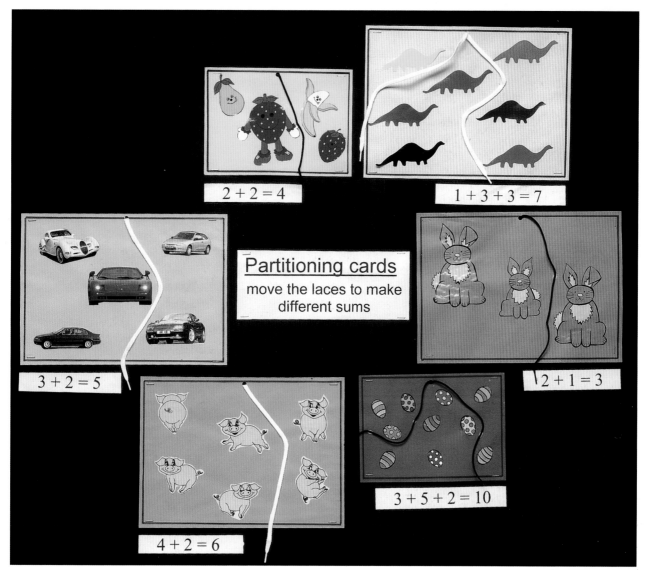

See Partitioning Cards on facing page

Number trios and commutative aspect

- Use egg boxes and rolled-up tissue paper as eggs. Talk to the children about ways to make sums from part-filling the egg box. For example,

$$4 + 2 = 6 \qquad 6 - 4 = 2$$
$$2 + 4 = 6 \qquad 6 - 0 = 6$$
$$6 - 2 = 4 \qquad 0 + 6 = 6$$

Get the children to write as many sums as they can about the eggs. What is the maximum number of sums which can be made from a six-hole egg box? What about other sizes of 'partitioned' food trays, such as bun trays or pencil holders? The insides of chocolate boxes or cardboard apple trays can be cut to any size as required. Collect as many different types as possible and use these for practical and written work.

- Use Stern rods or Cuisenaire to find all the members of number families.

Ways to make....

- Use Stern or Cuisenaire apparatus to play "Partners", making number bonds to 10. Ask one child to choose and hold up a rod, and the others have to guess which rod will go with that one to make a 10 rod. This can also be played using spinners or 10-sided die, where the children work in pairs, taking turns to call out the missing bond. Extend this by using groups of three rods. To make the link with subtraction, reword this game - hold up a 3 rod and ask, "Which rod has been taken away from 10 to leave this 3 rod?"

- Make a display of ten items which will change over a period of time, for example, flower buds **(see photograph)**, tadpoles, or eggs in an incubator.

  Check the display daily, and show the changes in a variety of ways which include pegboards, Multilink cubes, threaded beads, strips of coloured squared paper.

  Write sums to show how the display changes.

Play "Lilypads".
For two players, you will need:

    a baseboard
    2 dice
    10 counters each (a different colour for each
        player)

To play:
Players take turns to throw both dice and add the two together to find the total score. They each place counters on any of the lilypads on their own side of the pond which have numbers adding to that score. For example, if the total throw was 9, counters could be placed on 3, 4 and 2, or 6 and 3, etc. The first person to cover all their lilypads is the winner.

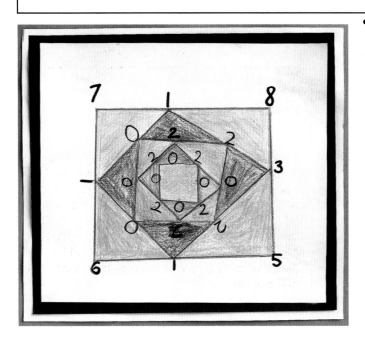

- **Play the "Diffy Game".** Ask the children to draw a square each and write one number between 1 and 10 at each corner. Put a dot half way along one side, find the difference between the two numbers at either end of that line and write this number beside the dot. Repeat for the other four sides.

  Now join the four dots to make a new square inside the original one. Put a dot halfway along one side of the new square and write beside it the difference between the two numbers at either end. Keep going until you end up with zero.
  Extend by using other shapes - does it still end up as zero? Why does it sometimes take more squares to get to a zero? **(See photographs to left and on the facing page.)**

This is what you do

First of all, draw a square and write a number at each corner. Then put a dot half way along each side.

Find the difference between the numbers at the corners and write that number next to the dot. Do that on all the sides of the square.

Then join the dots up and you will have a new square. Do the same thing again. Keep going until you get to zero.

by Jason and Kylie

We played
The Diffy Game!

Robert H

This is what we found out

We all did the squares and we got different numbers of small squares inside. We think this is because of the first 4 numbers we chose.

Rohan and William tried triangles but they got too small and they wouldn't go past 1,1,0. Florence did a triangle when she put even numbers on the corners.

The hexagons were good and they went on a long time.

by Shelagh and James

They get too small.

this one got too small.

Play a game of Trains.

Two children sit with a screen up between them (a propped-up book is fine) so that each cannot see what the other has done. Each then makes a train from any number of Multilink between 1 and 10 and the trains are then put next to each other. The difference between the two lengths is found. Ask the children to devise a points system, for example, same length = 0 points, difference of 1 = 1 point, difference of 2 = 2 points, etc., and have a class competition.

Play "A Handful of Beans".

Get each child in the group to pick up a handful of dried beans and estimate how many they have in their hand. Mark their estimates on a number line using a different coloured circle for each child. Then ask them to count how many beans they actually have, and mark that on the number line using the same colour. Now find the difference between the estimate and the actual number by counting on or back along the number line.

Missing numbers

- Let the children see you put a number of items, for example five, into a feely bag. Allow one child to feel the objects carefully, and then to turn away whilst another child removes a chosen number of objects. Ask the first child to work out how many were removed by feeling how many are left. This can be recorded in pictures or numbers.

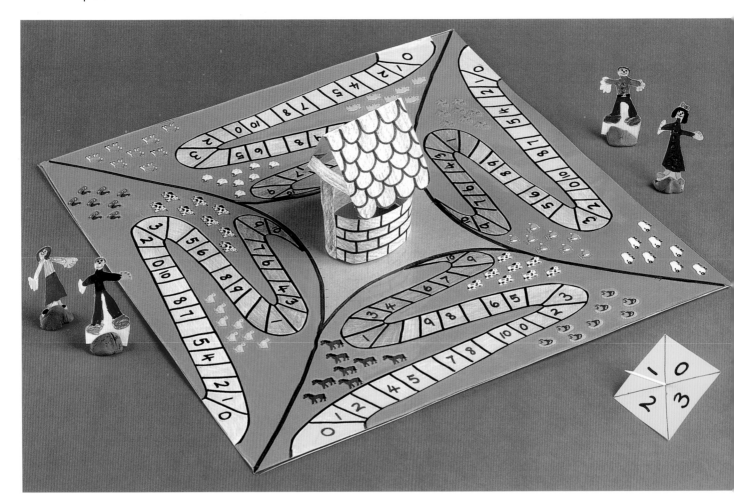

Play "Jack and Jill".

For four players, you will need:
      a baseboard **(see photograph)**
      a non-permanent OHP pen
      a spinner marked 0,1,2,3
      counters (the children could use drawings on card stuck into adhesive putty)

To play:

The object of the game is for the player to fill in the missing numbers on his/her path. Each child starts at the bottom of his/her hill, and moves the number of spaces shown on the spinner. If a child lands on a blank square, s/he writes in the appropriate number using the OHP pen. Players cannot proceed to the next section of the path toward the well until the previous one has been completed. This is done by 'tumbling' up and down - i.e. they may move forwards and backwards. The first to reach the well is the winner.

Money to 10p

Play "Match my Money!".

For up to four players, you will need:
2 sets of cards of different colours
set 1 - 2p, 5p (x 3), 10p (x 5)
(these amounts can be written, or shown by sticky paper coins)
set 2 - this set shows the equivalent amounts:
for the 2p card - 1p and 1p
for the 5p card - 1p and 1p and 1p and 2p
1p and 2p and 2p
1p and 1p and 1p and 1p and 1p
for the 10p card - 5p and 5p
5p and 2p and 2p and 1p, etc.

Use these cards to play Pairs.

• Using parent helpers, go shopping for penny sweets in small groups to a local shop with 10p in pennies. (If this is impractical, buy a selection and sell them in school.) Once back in school, record in drawings what has been purchased. The wide range of different purchases should encourage discussion - bargain hunters may come back with ten sweets, while impulse buyers will probably buy one large packet of something!

Make copies of the sweets purchased using playdough (mini biscuit cutters are useful for this) and recreate the stock in the shop to continue simple transactions. Ask the children to buy one item, two items, etc. The concept of "change" will inevitably arise. The children need some idea of equivalence before they can grasp this. If possible, borrow older pupils to be shopkeepers. Again, record simply in drawing form.

Play "Nursery Rhymes".
For up to four players you will need:
4 game boards
plastic money
2 dice, each marked 1p, 1p, 2p, 3p, 4p, 5p.

To play:
Players take turns to throw the dice, and then take that amount of money from the central pile - the Bank. They put these coins in the places marked in the circles on their picture. Extra coins can be kept to use on later turns. More than one coin can be placed on any circle to make the total if required, for example, 3p would be made from a 2p and a 1p piled on top. The first player to fill all his/her circles is the winner.

NUMBERS 10 - 20

Place value

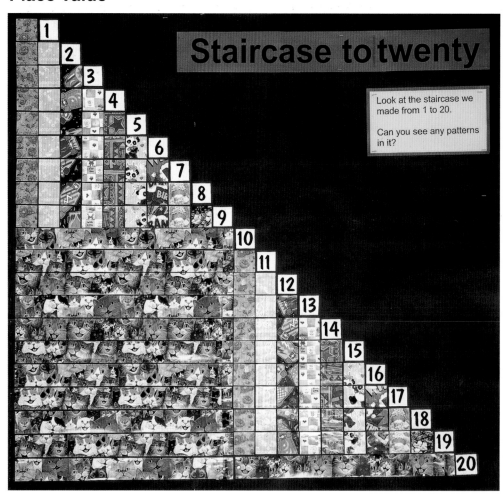

Staircase to twenty

Look at the staircase we made from 1 to 20.

Can you see any patterns in it?

- Get the children to make Cuisenaire and Stern staircases when introducing the concept of place value, using a 10 rod for each of the "teen" numbers between 10 and 20.

  Build your own staircase using strips of wrapping paper **(see photograph left).**

- Use small stickers or stamps to make rows of objects of different lengths on squared paper. Ask the children to count one of the rows and find the total in that row. Talk about whether it was awkward counting accurately. Show how grouping in tens makes it much easier to count quickly by getting the children to colour the first ten objects in each row, and then find the total by counting on.

Play "Dinosaurs".
For two players, you will need:
    a set of 10 cards with the numbers from
        0 - 9 written in red
    a set of 10 cards with the number 10 written
        on each in black and with a picture of
        a dinosaur on the reverse side.
(On each of the above cards, write the word "match" and an arrow - **see illustration**)

To play:
Separate the cards into dinosaurs/non dinosaurs and put the two piles face down on the table. The children take turns to turn over a dinosaur card and a plain card and add them together mentally. They then overlap the two cards to check whether their answer was correct. If they are right, they keep the card. If they are wrong, they return the cards to the bottom of the piles. The child who collects the most dinosaurs is the winner.

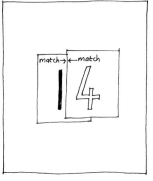

Base and grouping work

Games are an ideal, practical and enjoyable way for children to gain experience of grouping materials. The principle is always the same: when an agreed number of items has been collected, they must be exchanged for one item which has the same value. Ideas are as varied as your imagination. Use stickers and pictures cut from wrapping paper to make the games. To practise grouping in different numbers, change the base by altering the numbers on the dice (largest number to be one less than the base the children will be working in), and then change game boards if required.

Base 4 car game

win 4 wheels and exchange for a car

win 4 cars and exchange for a garage

the first to get 2 garages is the winner !

use a spinner marked 0,1,2,3

GARAGE

Play "Garages" (base 4).
For two players you will need:
      16 tyres and 16 cars (cut out from magazines and stuck on card)
      4 cards with one garage drawn on each
      I die marked 1,1,2,2,3,3.

To play:
The children take turns to throw the dice, and collect the same number of tyres as the dice shows. When a child has four tyres, s/he swaps them for a car. For example, if a child has three tyres and throws a two, which makes five altogether, s/he then has to change four tyres for a card, and is left with one odd tyre to keep for the next round. When a child has four cars, s/he must exchange for a garage. The first child to have two garages is the winner.

• Give the children practice in finding the difference between 10 and a number in the teens, for example, 10 and 15. Help them to see the pattern. If they know that 10 + 5 = 15, then the difference between 10 and 15 must be 5.

Number lines

- Make a "daisy chain" number line. Print or cut out yellow circles for the centres of the daisies, and then print the white petals around them, leaving the first one bare to represent zero (making sure that the petal size allows you to fit 10 petals around the circumference of the yellow centre).

When the daisies from 0 to 10 have been printed, ask the children what comes next, and whether they can think of a way to make '11'. They will suggest using two daisies: 10 + 1 = 11.

- To make a number line which includes negative numbers, construct a giant thermometer - perhaps on the floor.

- Play a game (two players) to help with number recognition. Draw a row of 'parking spaces', numbered from 11 to 20. One child chooses a number, but does not say it. The other child 'drives' a toy car into one of the spaces. If the number is too low the other child puts, say, a red counter on the space. The other child tries again. If the number is too high, a counter of a different colour is placed on the space. The game continues until the right number is found.

Odds and evens and counting in 2s

- Count objects in 2s - socks, gloves, eyes.

- **Sorting Odds and Evens**
  Give each child a number and ask them to discover whether their number is odd or even and to find a way to prove it. Extend this by setting groups of children challenges: for example, to sort their names into sets with odd and even numbers of letters.

  (See photographs left and on facing page.)

24

Refer to Sorting Odds and Evens on the facing page

- Design a dot-to-dot picture by placing tracing paper over an image and putting dots at strategic points such as junctions. Number it, ensuring that the picture can only be completed by joining the odd or even numbers in the correct order.

Play "See-Saw, Margery Daw".
For two players, you will need:
- a simple, home-made miniature see-saw
- I die
- a set of counters
- 2 pictures (a boy and a girl) to represent children on the see-saw, attached with adhesive putty

To play:
The first child chooses whether s/he wishes to be the boy or the girl, and puts that end of the see-saw down. The children take turns to throw the dice which will tell them how many moves of the see-saw they should make. But before moving, they must predict whether their person will end up in the air or down on the ground. If they are correct, they may take a counter. The winner is the child who collects the most counters after a pre-arranged number of turns.

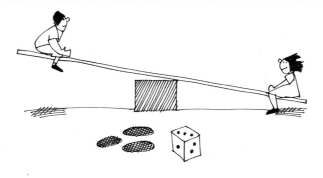

25

- Ask the children to find examples of odd and even numbers in their own homes (**see photograph left**).

Ordering

- Find the effect of changing the order of two identical sets of numbers written along two parallel lines, each number being joined to its partner on the opposite line. How can we ensure that the resulting patterns turn out symmetrically?

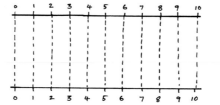

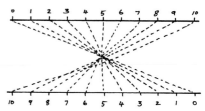

Play the "What's my number?" game.
For two players you will need:
    a playing board **(see illustration)**
    a piece of paper and a pencil
    a set of small cards reading "too high" and "too low"

To play:
One child chooses a number between 10 and 20 and writes it secretly on a piece of paper. The second child tries to guess this number and the first child puts a "too high" or "too low" label in the space under the stated number until the correct number is deduced. The children then swap places.

26

Play "Order! Order!".
For up to four players, you will need:
>   2 sets of cards with numbers from 10 to 20
>   2 larger cards, one with 10 written on it and the other with 20 written on it.

To play:
Three cards are dealt to each player, and the remainder are placed face down in a pile in the centre of the table. The two larger cards are placed side by side in the middle, and the players take it in turns to place their cards on top of these. They may choose which pile to place a card on, one pile going in order from 10 to 20, and the other in reverse order from 20 to 10. If a player cannot go, they must take a card from the pile in the centre. The winner is the first to lay down all his cards.

Number bonds

- **Get the children to make pictures out of felt,** to which they can add parts such as the spots on a cow or the windows on a train. Make a display from these, where they can come and put on as many spots as they choose (felt adheres to felt), and then use the cards to write a sum about the picture.

- Look at patterns of addition, for example,

$$2 + 3 + 5 = 10$$
$$2 + 5 + 3 = 10$$
$$3 + 2 + 5 = 10$$
$$3 + 5 + 2 = 10$$
$$5 + 2 + 3 = 10$$
$$5 + 3 + 2 = 10$$

What happens if you add these numbers vertically?
Write down the pairs of numbers which, when added together, make a total of 10.

Use these:
  - to make a "curved stitching" design **(see illustration)**
  - to make a pattern by joining these pairs along two parallel lines
  - to make a pattern by joining these pairs along two non-parallel lines
  - as co-ordinates.

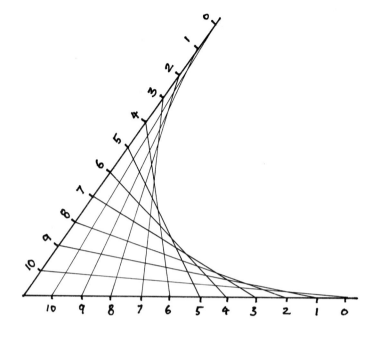

- Examine some dice and ask the children to find out as much as they can about how the numbers are arranged. When they have found that opposite faces add to seven, get them to draw a net of a cube and write in the numbers in the correct places to make a proper die before they assemble it (there are two possibilities). Now, working with a partner, put two dice together with two faces touching, and find the total of all the faces now showing. How many different totals can they make? Ask them to arrange the dice to make the largest/smallest totals.

Dice games

Throwing dice, doing something with the score, and recording the results, provides children with enjoyable practice in handling numbers.

Activity 1

Ask the children to work in pairs, and give each couple a piece of squared paper and two dice. Ask them to take turns to throw the dice, add the score and record in the form of a block graph. Why were no "ones" thrown? Why is there a peak at the number 7? Some children may wish to extend this to using three dice to find where the peak is then.

Activity 2

As in Activity 1, but this time the children record the difference between the two dice scores.

Activity 3

As in Activity 1, but using only one die.

Activity 4

Play a board game such as Snakes and Ladders using two dice, and vary the rules, perhaps by giving the children the choice between finding the total or the difference, depending on their requirements in the game.

Activity 5

Use the numbers on the opposite sides of the die to practise addition and subtraction. Extend this by finding the total of the odd numbers and the even numbers, and the sum of all the numbers on the die.

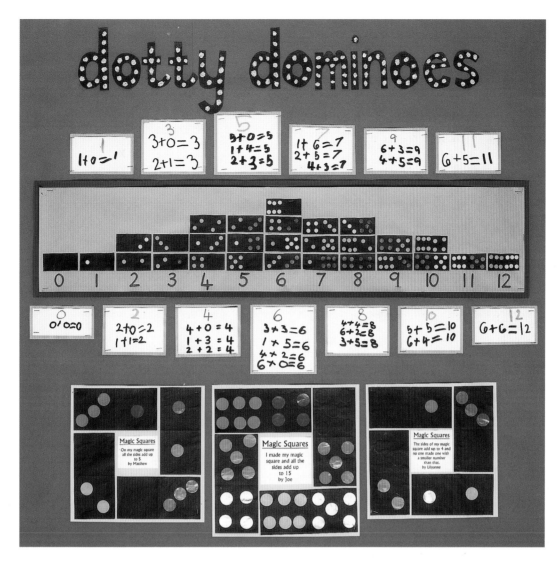

- Make 3 x 3 magic squares using the numbers 1 to 9, where each row, diagonal and column, add to a total of 15. Extend this by adding three to each of the numbers in the first square - is the resulting square still magic? Try adding the two squares together - is it still magic? Show the children some magic squares and let them practise using them.

- **Dotty Dominoes**
  Use dominoes to further investigate magic squares. Firstly, allow the children to familiarise themselves with dominoes by playing the game and sorting **(see photograph above)**, and then ask them to make a magic square using four dominoes - each side of the square must add to the same total. Challenge them to make squares with the largest/smallest possible totals along each side.

- Ask the children to find the answers when doubling all the numbers from 1 to 10. Look at these 'doubled' numbers - is there a pattern? Why? Show them how to use this knowledge when adding two numbers which are very close together, for example 8 + 9 (double the 8 and add 1, or double the 9 and subtract 1).

Play "Take 20".
For two players you will need:
      a set of cards with pairs of numbers which add up to 20 (written one on each side)

To play:
Spread the cards out on the table. Player 1 chooses a card and points it out to player 2, who then has to guess which number is written on the reverse. Player 2 then turns the card over and, if correct, s/he keeps the card. If incorrect, s/he replaces it. The winner is the child who collects the most cards by the end of the game.

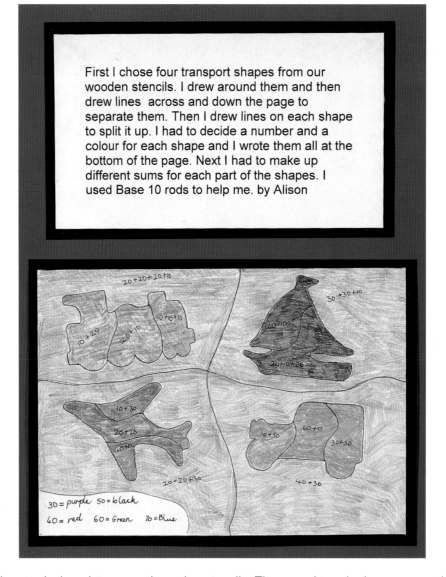

First I chose four transport shapes from our wooden stencils. I drew around them and then drew lines across and down the page to separate them. Then I drew lines on each shape to split it up. I had to decide a number and a colour for each shape and I wrote them all at the bottom of the page. Next I had to make up different sums for each part of the shapes. I used Base 10 rods to help me. by Alison

- Ask the children to design picture puzzles using stencils. They need to take into account the need for realism. For example, if the boat needs to be black, the sum written in the boat shape must total the number which represents black in the key.

  To extend more able children, encourage them to overlap the shapes to make a more complex design. Photocopy these and get the children to complete each other's pictures.

Play "What's My Sum?".
For two players, you will need:
    a gameboard
    a pencil

To play:
Player 1 holds up the gameboard, with theanswers facing him/her. Player 1 then calls out one of the numbers s/he can see, and player 2 has to find the sum which will produce that answer. S/he then sticks a pencil through that hole and if it is the hole next to the number called out, player 1 calls out "Yes!". The children can devise a scoring system if they wish to.

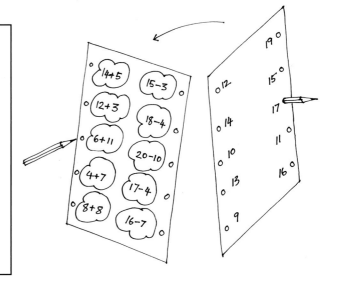

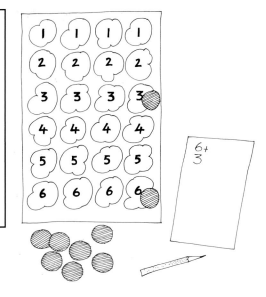

Play "Twenty, twenty".

For two players you will need:
- a gameboard
- counters
- one piece of paper and a pencil

To play:

Players take turns in placing counters on numbers, with only one counter on each number. As a number is covered, it is added to the total which is being kept by the players. The winner is the player who manages to bring the total exactly to 20. If a player takes the total over 20, s/he is the loser.

Finding the 10

This game will help children to acquire the skill of identifying pairs of numbers which add together to make 10.

Play "Ten Spotting".

For two players, you will need:
- pencil and paper each
- 20 cards - each with a car drawn on it (or made with wrapping paper pictures) with the number plate of each visible - see line drawing. (Give each car a number plate which incorporates a number bond to ten, plus another single digit number, e.g. 872, 565, 406.)

To play:

The cards are placed face down. Both children take a card and immediately look for the two numbers which add together to make 10. They then write '10 + ...', and add the other digit to complete the sum. Therefore, if the number plate was 595, they would have written '10 + 9 = 19'. The child with the highest score wins both cards. Play continues until all cards have been used. The winner is the child with the most cards.

Commutative law

This can be shown most clearly using Stern or Cuisenaire apparatus, for example,

$$3 + 6 = 6 + 3$$

Show the children this and then allow them to investigate using apparatus.

- Use hundred squares and number lines to show the commutative nature of addition. Draw a circle around the number 8. Count on 6 and draw a square around the number

$$8 + 6 = 14$$

Now draw a circle around the number 6, count on 8 and see where you land.

$$6 + 8 = 14$$

- Make Addition Tables and find as many patterns as you can. Is there any symmetry in the table? Ask the children to find a reason for this.

Number stories

Discuss the places where numbers are to be seen every day - clocks, streets, calendars, newspapers, on the television, shops, etc. Find numbers on packets, in books, on clothing, by looking out through the window. Could any of these numbers be replaced with a word without confusing everyone? For example, would it matter if a car was called "Henry" instead of having a registration plate?

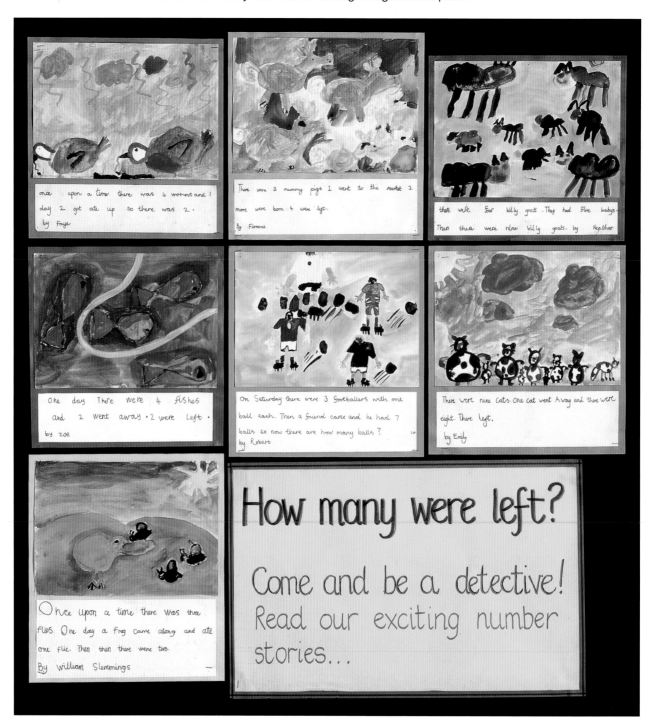

- **Make up stories involving numbers, and illustrate them.** Alternatively, ask the children to tell a story from a picture.

- Tell the children number stories with deliberate mistakes in them, and ask them to spot the error. For example, "When I went to the shop to spend my 20p pocket money, I bought three pencils which cost 3p each, and then I had 9p left over to buy a notebook."

NUMBERS TO 100 AND OVER

Number line, 100 square and estimation activities

- Ask the children to 'collect' numbers from their environment, for example, "Our classroom has 29 chairs in it", or "Six people sit at our table". Discuss when we can use numbers accurately, and when we can approximate. For example, ask the children how many days there are in January, or how many of the class are wearing shoes with laces. Then ask them how many toys they have in their bedroom, or how many books there are in the bookcase.

- Talk to the children about words such as 'centurion', 'century', 'centipede' and 'centimeter'.

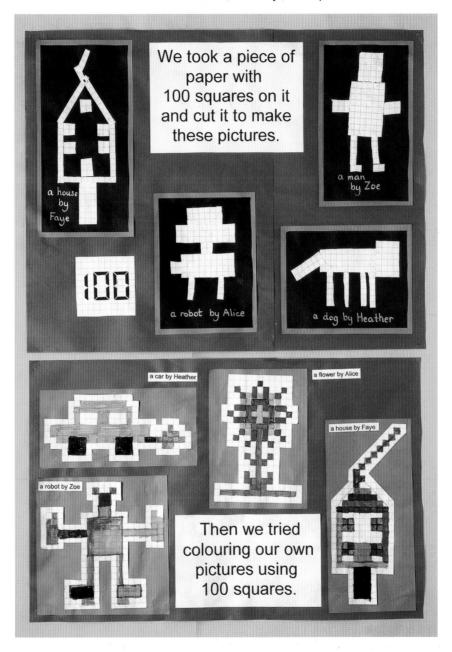

We took a piece of paper with 100 squares on it and cut it to make these pictures.

a house by Faye

a man by Zoe

a robot by Alice

a dog by Heather

a car by Heather

a flower by Alice

a house by Faye

a robot by Zoe

Then we tried colouring our own pictures using 100 squares.

- Give the children 10 x 10 pieces of squared paper and get them to cut them any way they choose, along the lines, and then reassemble them. Talk about the resulting shapes and make sure that the children realise that, whatever the shape may be, there are still 100 squares in it **(see photograph)**.

- Make and display collections of 100 items, such as dried peas, stamps, pencils, Lego, rice, buttons, biscuits (in packets!). Put any loose objects in pots covered with Clingfilm so that the contents can be seen. Talk about the collection, and use it to count in 100s. Extend it to include a length of wool 100cm long, and a bag of sand weighing 100g.

- Using 10 x 10 pieces of squared paper, get the children to colour strips of 10. Cut out the strips, and let the children arrange them, stick them on to paper and then write sums about their arrangement **(see photograph).**

- Talk about large numbers, and what sort of things are counted in these numbers. For example,
  - 10s might be the age of their parents and grandparents
  - 100s might be the total number of children in the school, or days in a year
  - 1000s might be the cost of a new car, or the number of miles to America
  - 10,000s might be the cost of a house.
  - Find examples of these large numbers in newspapers and price lists.

- Use wrapping paper which has a small, repeating design, such as lots of cats, to estimate larger numbers. Challenge the children to find a quick way to check their estimation. One way to do this would be to spot the repeating pattern. Another would be to count how many images are in a small square, and then see how many of those squares fit into the whole piece.

- When colouring the area of a hand on squared paper, ask the children to colour in strips or patches of 10 squares to make the counting easier.

- Go for a walk to study house numbers in the area. Are they consecutive/across the road/arranged in a different fashion? Are there are numbers which are missing? Are any houses not numbered? Why not? How would a delivery person know the number of that house? Find out who in the class lives in the street with most/least houses, or with the lowest/highest numbers.

Come and make a number!

10 20 30 40 50 60 70 80 90 100

- Give each child a square piece of card to take home and find ten objects which can be stuck on to it, for example, ten birthday candles or dried flowers. When they bring these to school, cover them with clear adhesive-backed plastic, and use to count in 10s, to look at 100, to make a 100 square, for addition and subtraction in 10s, etc. **(see photograph above).**

- Ask older children in the school to design and make games which involve working with larger numbers **(see examples in photographs above and right and on page 2).**

- Give each child a hundred square and ask them to find and colour the first three numbers of a sequence, for example, 100, 89, 78. Talk about the resulting pattern and ask the children to predict and colour the rest of the numbers in the sequence.

- Make simple "slide rules" using two strips of 2cm squared paper. Label each of these to 20 and use them to solve addition and subtraction problems.

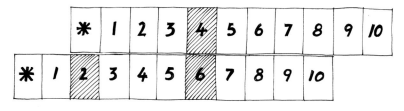

2 + 4 = 6

- Give a group of children a 10 x 10 piece of centimetre square paper. Confirm that there are 100 small squares, and then ask them to cover the piece of paper with Cuisennaire rods and then write sums based on this.

Negative numbers should be introduced in context - such as through work on temperature (see page 49).

Place value
- Give the children some 10 x 10 pieces of squared paper and ask them to colour the paper in strips of 10. Then stick 10 of these on a larger rectangle to make 1000. Ask the children to show other numbers by putting circles of coloured wool around the squares. For example, 250 would be shown by putting the wool around two 100 squares and half of a third one.

- Select a number, for example 23, and find as many different ways as possible to show it. Use both free materials to show grouping, for example, two sets of 10 shells and three odd ones, and structured apparatus such as Stern, base 10 mats, interlocking cubes, Cuisenaire, money, abacus.

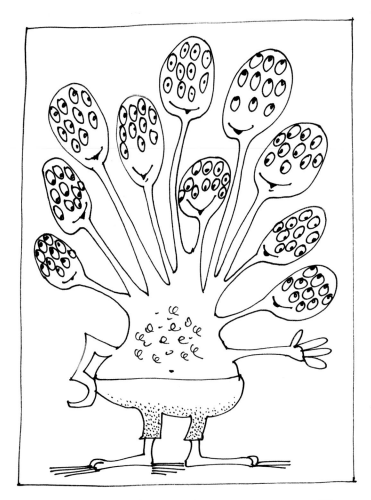

Play "The Monster game".
For up to four players, you will need:
     40 eyes (use counters)
     40 heads with 10 eyes drawn
          on each (ask the children
          to draw these)
     4 whole 10-headed monsters
          (ask the children to draw
          these)
     1 - 9 die

To play:
Players take turns to roll the die and collect eyes, exchanging them for a head when they have 10. They continue to collect heads until they have 10, which they then exchange for a whole monster.
The first child to get a monster is the winner.

36

Play "Highest and Lowest".

For up to four players you will need:

a set of 36 cards, comprising four sets of cards numbered 1 - 9
a set of four cards numbered 0.

To play:

Put the two sets of cards in two piles in the centre of the table. Each player then takes two cards from the numbered card pile and one zero card. First the aim is to arrange their cards to make the highest number possible, which they must be able to read aloud. A point is given for the highest. Then the numbers are re-arranged to make the lowest possible number, which they must be able to read aloud, and another point is given. For example, if a child picks the numbers 3, 5 and 0, the highest number will be 530 and the lowest will be 305. (035 or any combination with zero first is unacceptable.) The winner is the player with the highest number of points after an agreed number of rounds. To extend, take three cards and a zero card.

Play "Spin and Win".

For up to four players, you will need:

Base 10 materials
a spinner marked 0, 0, 00, 00
a die marked 0, 0, 1, 1, 2, 3.

To play:

The players take turns to spin the spinner and throw the die. The scores are then put together to make a number, for example 00 on the spinner and 3 on the die would make 300, and the player can collect 300 of the Base 10 materials, i.e. three flats. If all zeros are thrown, nothing may be collected. If the player reaches a stage where s/he has 10 longs, s/he should automatically exchange for a 100 flat, and the same again when 10 x 100 is reached. Notation cards are useful to set the materials out on as the players collect them. The winner could be the player who has collected the most in a given time limit, or the first to reach a total score, e.g. 10,000.

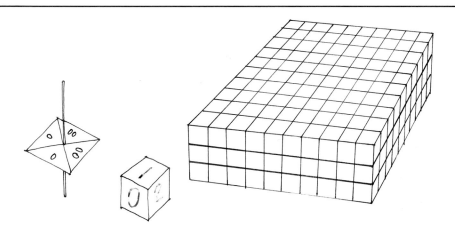

Addition and Subtraction

- Using the back of two light plastic trays, stick on hooks and transfers (or stickers) to make a hoop-la game involving addition of multiples of ten and units.

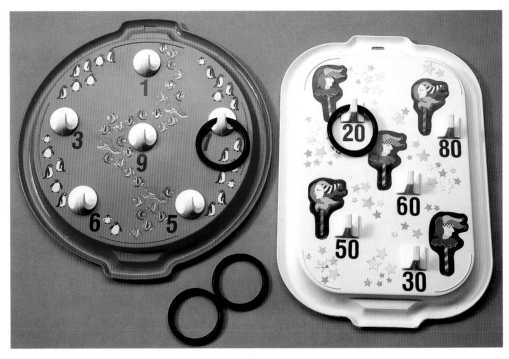

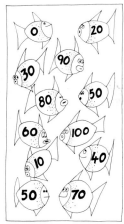

- Make "Colour by number" pictures. Give the children a pattern on which you have written pairs of numbers which add to 100. They then find the matching pairs and colour each pair.

1	2	3	4	5	6	7	8	9	10
11	12	13	14	15	16	17	18	19	20
21	22	23	24	25	26	27	28	29	30
31	32	33	34	35	36	37	38	39	40
41	42	43	44	45	46	47	48	49	50
51	52	53	54	55	56	57	58	59	60
61	62	63	64	65	66	67	68	69	70
71	72	73	74	75	76	77	78	79	80
81	82	83	84	85	86	87	88	89	90
91	92	93	94	95	96	97	98	99	100

Play "10, 20, 30".
For up to four players you will need:
    a gameboard
    1 dice with 10, 20, 30, 40, 50 and 60
    1 dice with + (x 3) and - (x 3) signs
    1 1-9 dice
    counters (as markers)

To play:
Game 1 - The aim is to be the first to land exactly on 100. The players use all three dice and take it in turns to throw, totalling their score and moving their counter by this amount.
On the final row, the 10s dice need not be used. If the final throw is too large (for example, 33 when only 21 is needed to land on 100), that turn is missed.

Game 2 - The aim is to land on 100 again, but this time omitting the subtraction/addition dice and only using addition.

Game 3 - The aim is to land on 1 by starting at 100 and only using subtraction.

Game 4 - The aim is to be the first to get to 100 and then back to 1.

Money to £1

Our Money Family
by Natasha, Nicholas and Jason

I made a dog called Fido Fifty.
I used 1p, 2p and 5p.

by Jason

My man is called Nick Ninety.
I used 10p, 5p and 2p.

by Nicholas

I made Nanny Ninety.
I used 1p, 2p, 5p and 20p.

by Natasha

- **Practise coin rubbing.** When the children are proficient, challenge them to make "Money People" using coins which total a given amount, such as "Freddy Fifty" or "Samantha Seventy".

- Talk about the value of money, and what is meant by the terms *expensive, cheap, good value, a bargain,* etc. Look through catalogues, and ask the children to write shopping lists or cut out objects they would buy if they had a given amount to spend **(see photograph right).**

Our group pretended that we had £5, £10 and £20 to spend and we chose 3 things we would like to buy.

Our group looked through the catalogues and chose the things we would buy if we had £100 to spend. We added up on a calculator.

Play "In the Money".

For two players, you will need:
  paper and pencil each
  3 dice
  1 gameboard

To play:

Players take turns to throw all the dice, and then make up a sum using these three numbers. For example, if they threw 1, 4 and 6, they could have 1 + 4 + 6 = 11, or 6 - 4 + 1 = 3, etc. They then look on the gameboard to find their prize. The winner is the first to earn £1.

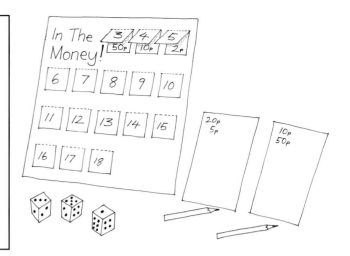

Multiplication and Division

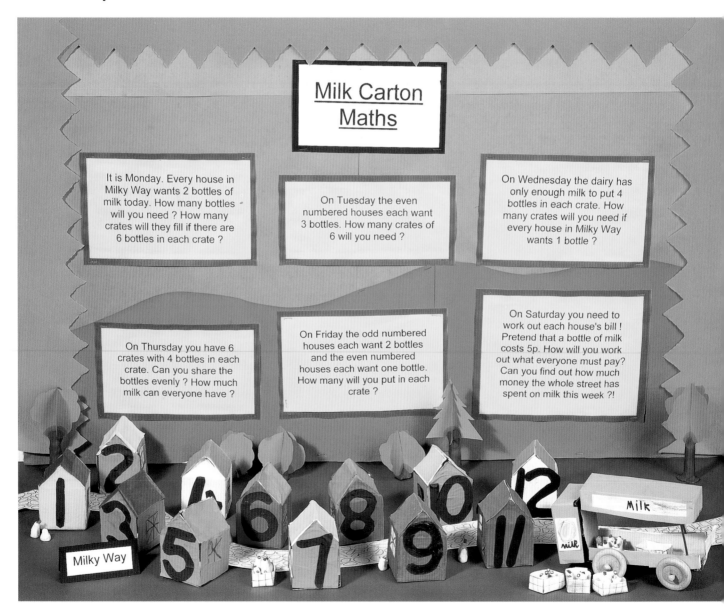

Milk Carton Maths

It is Monday. Every house in Milky Way wants 2 bottles of milk today. How many bottles will you need ? How many crates will they fill if there are 6 bottles in each crate ?

On Tuesday the even numbered houses each want 3 bottles. How many crates of 6 will you need ?

On Wednesday the dairy has only enough milk to put 4 bottles in each crate. How many crates will you need if every house in Milky Way wants 1 bottle ?

On Thursday you have 6 crates with 4 bottles in each crate. Can you share the bottles evenly ? How much milk can everyone have ?

On Friday the odd numbered houses each want 2 bottles and the even numbered houses each want one bottle. How many will you put in each crate ?

On Saturday you need to work out each house's bill ! Pretend that a bottle of milk costs 5p. How will you work out what everyone must pay? Can you find out how much money the whole street has spent on milk this week ?!

- **Make a milk carton village (see photograph).** The children can then use this to explore multiplication and division in a practical situation by using the Plasticine milk bottles to solve problems.

- See if anyone can get close to 100 by doubling - 1,2,4,8, etc. What is the best number to start with?

- Make use of objects which the children bring into the classroom, for example, a skateboard, which could serve as a stimulus for work such as counting in 4s (number of wheels), and subtraction through puzzles such as "There are three skateboards, but each one has lost a wheel. How many wheels are left?"

- Give each child a piece of squared paper which has been divided randomly into rows from 1 to 5 squares wide. Ask the children to colour a pattern in each strip, using a different number each time. Get them to write a repeated addition sum for each row, which leads to talking about multiplication as "lots of" **(see photograph).**

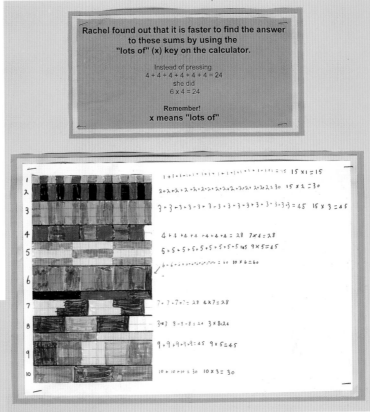

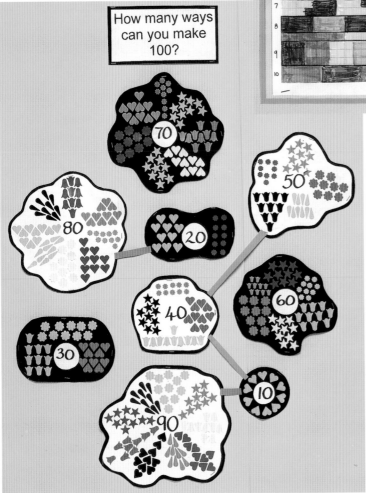

- Make a wall display based on the idea that the children have to find pairs of numbers (all multiples of 10) which will add together to make 100.

- Play Circle Games. Ask the children to stand in a circle and count round in 2s, each child calling out the next number in the pattern. Begin by counting to 20, and then starting back at 2. Any child who can't answer within a given time has to sit down. Get faster as the game progresses! Extend to 100 when the children are ready. Play the same game counting in 5s and 10s.

PRACTICAL APPLICATIONS OF LARGER NUMBERS

Length

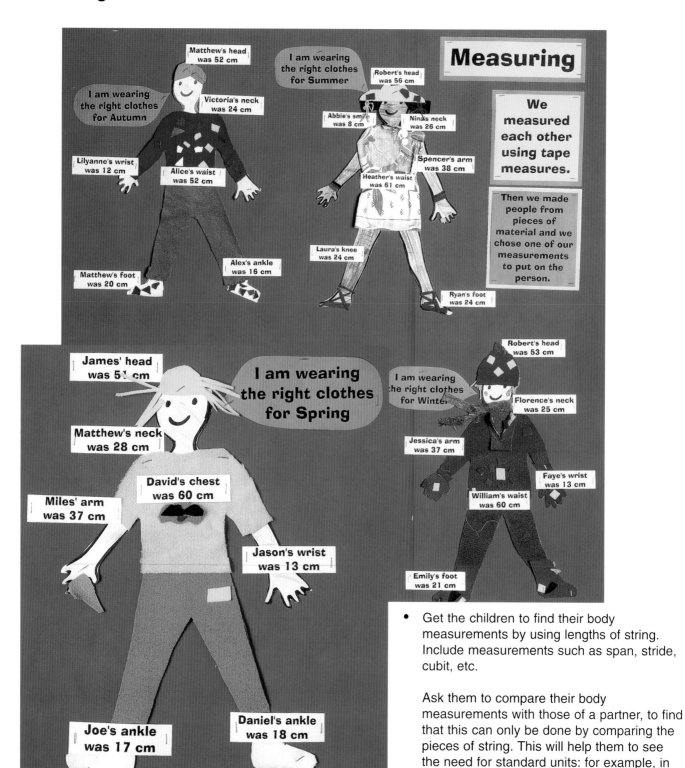

- Get the children to find their body measurements by using lengths of string. Include measurements such as span, stride, cubit, etc.

  Ask them to compare their body measurements with those of a partner, to find that this can only be done by comparing the pieces of string. This will help them to see the need for standard units: for example, in order to find out immediately which child has the longest hand span, we need to know its length in centimetres.

- Colour in strips of 10cm when recording the height of the children in the class to encourage them to count in 10s. Introduce a metre as being equivalent to 10 x 10cm strips, i.e. 100cm.

Meet
Tom and Cherry!

We used
Michael and Jasmine's
measurements to make Tom
and Cherry.

- **Use the measurements of two children to make stuffed figures.** Write their measurements on cards and tie them on to the bodies **(see photograph).**

- Choose three items to measure (small, medium, large) such as a pencil, the length of a piano and the width of the playground. Talk about different tools and units of measurement. After much discussion and demonstration, ask the children to work in groups, and measure the items using appropriate equipment and units of measurement. Compare the groups' results.

A pencil was _____ long.

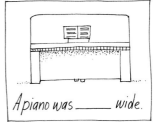

A piano was _____ wide.

The playground was _____ long.

- Borrow a skeleton, perhaps from a local secondary school, and ask the children to compare the lengths of their bones with those of the skeleton.

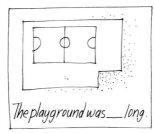

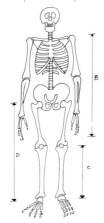

	me	skeleton
A		
B		
C		
D		

- Find the length of a loaf of bread after measuring one slice.

43

Weight

- Ensure that the children have access to a range of measuring equipment, including balances with weights, scales with dials, spring balances and digital scales if possible.

- Make a display of "things that weigh the same as 1g", "things that weigh the same as 10g", and so on, using standard units up to 1kg.
  Draw the objects and make into a class book

- Set up a fruit stall. Include play dough (or Plasticine) vegetables (carrots, leeks, apples, bananas, etc.) and ask the children to weigh out a specific amount, for example: 1kg of potatoes, ½kg of apples or 200g of tomatoes. How much do four apples weigh? How many bananas can I buy for 50p? Price the food per kilogram and let the children total their shopping bills.

- Bring in a collection of food packages. Include tinned food, cereal cartons, sugar, etc. Ask the children to compare the weights of the foods by handling them, and then by checking the weights written on the labels.
  Order the packages from lightest to heaviest. Point out the fact that the smaller items may not be the lightest, and the larger things may not be the heaviest.

  Try to find out how much of the weight is packaging by removing the contents and weighing the food separately. Once the children have had sufficient experience of handling weights of food, ask them to bring empty packages into school and make a wall display.

- **Set up a Post Office in the classroom (see photograph on facing page).** Prepare some wrapped mystery parcels, making sure to include a small parcel that is heavy (a box filled with Plasticine works well), and a large parcel that is light, such as an empty cereal carton.

  On the front of each parcel, make a clear plastic window for "stamps" to be inserted. The children have to calculate the weight of the parcel, and then the cost of posting it, basing the price on 10g = 1p. They then make up the appropriate amount using pre-printed stamps to the value of 50p, 20p, 10p, 5p and 1p. This could be increased in difficulty according to the ability of the children, for example 10g = 20p.

Set up a Post Office in the classrom - see text on facing page

Time

- Read *Too Many Clocks* by Pat Hutchins, which is a good starting point for a discussion on the need for standardised time.

- Talk about different measurements of time from smallest to largest - seconds, minutes, hours, days, weeks, months, years, decades, centuries. Discuss the seasons, and more informal measures such as weekends, mornings, afternoons, fortnights, etc.

- To extend children who have an advanced understanding of time, set them challenges such as: "How many seconds in a day?" or "How many days in five years?" They could use a calculator for these investigations.

- If practical, visit Greenwich, or a local clock museum.

- Tell the children ways of counting approximately in seconds, for example, by saying "one elephant, two elephants...etc." Play games, such as asking the children to close their eyes and to put their hands up when they think ten seconds has elapsed.

- **Make a shadow clock** and mark the changes every half hour. Record this on a series of blank clocks.

A season in our school

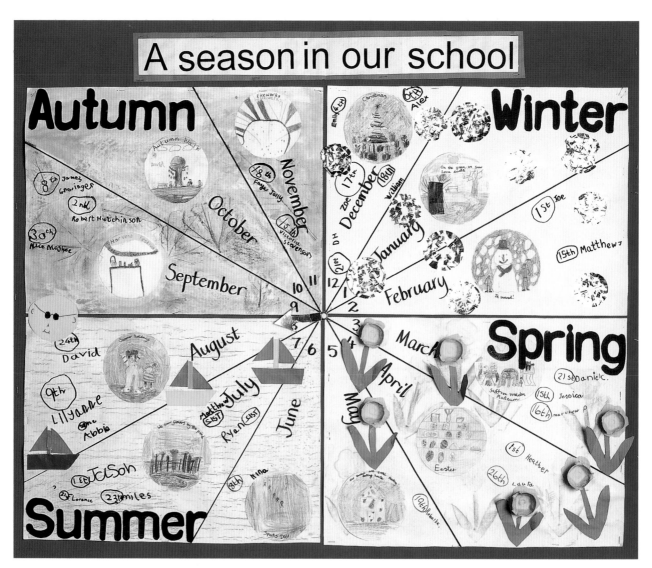

- Make a seasons calendar. Use four large sheets of paper, dividing each into three sections as in the photograph. At the beginning of the school year, get the children to write their birthdays in the appropriate month. As each season arrives, the children whose birthdays fall in that season decorate that section of the calendar. The circles depict an event which occurs in each month, such as Bonfire Night **(see photograph above)**.

- Get the children to carry out investigations into how many activities they can carry out in a given time, for example, "I can skip – times in 30 seconds."

In 30 seconds I can.....	
write my name	____ times
skip	____ times
bounce a ball	____ times
count to	

- Reverse this activity by asking the children to find out how long it takes for them to carry one particular activity, for example, "It took me – seconds to run round the playground."

- Ask the children to estimate how many minutes an activity such as writing their news will take.

- Construct a display to make children aware of the different ways in which time can be conveyed, using digital and analogue time, for example 3.45, a quarter to four, 15 minutes to 4.

- Play 'pairs' games, or Snap, using pictures of analogue and digital clocks.

- **Make enlargements of the times of children's television programmes** from the newspaper and ask questions, for example, "How long is – on for?", or "What time does – start?" "Can you show these times on an analogue clock?"

CHILDRENS T.V.	
3.30 p.m	Mouse House
3.35 p.m	Playway
3.50 p.m	Bear Stories
4.20 p.m	Arthur
4.35 p.m	Round th
5.00 p.m	News

Angle

- **Play "Robots"**, where children work with partners and one has to direct another around the room by using half and quarter turns. Ask them to record the route on squared paper. This can be extended during P.E. lessons, by investigating turns and pathways (**see photograph**).

- Show the children a square, and talk about the 'square corners'. Make right angle measures by folding a piece of paper, and find where they occur in the classroom. Classify angles in terms of 'greater than a right angle', 'less than a right angle', etc.

  Open up the pieces of paper, and examine the folds. Putting a pin in the centre of the cross, and a spot on one of the folds, rotate the paper so that the children can see that four right angles make a complete turn.

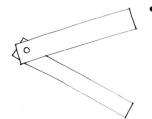

- Using Geostrips, or strips of card joined with split pins, help the children to understand an angle as a measure of turning. Place the two strips on top of each other, and then open them to make a right angle. Do the same to make angles *less than*, and then *more than*, a right angle.

- Get the children to make paper directional compasses with an arm attached using a split pin. Investigate the angles turned through when following instructions, for example, "clockwise, from North to East". A similar game can be played using a clock face: "At what angle are the hands when it is 3 o'clock?"

- Make rotational patterns based on half and quarter turns.

- Cut up juice drink cartons to find how many one-quarter turn (right) angles there are in a cuboid.

- Now introduce the concept of degrees, which are like little steps. Explain that there are 90° in a right angle, 180° in a half turn, and 360° in a whole turn. Play guessing games, where the children estimate the size of angles greater and less than 90°.

- LOGO provides an excellent opportunity to use 90° angles. Use an overhead projector sheet to draw a simple maze, with treasure at the centre. Place this sheet on the monitor, and challenge the children to write a pathway through the maze to reach the treasure.

  Using the same technique, the children can also draw their own maps of the classroom, and challenge each other to write a pathway from the bookcase to the door, for example **(see photograph left)**.

Temperature

- Make a **"Temperature Tree"**. Draw a large tree with a leaf outline to correspond to each day of the month, and write the date on each. Devise a key using colours to represent a range of temperature, depending on the season. Read the temperature daily and record on the tree by colouring a leaf in the appropriate colour **(see photograph above)**.

- After explaining that measurement of temperature is called *degrees*, enlarge a drawing of a thermometer with a clear scale and explain the gradations.

- On a photocopy of a thermometer, record the daily temperature for a week or two during each season. Hopefully, the winter will provide some minus numbers, which can reinforce children's understanding of negative numbers.

- Enlarge and study a weather forecast from a newspaper - look at the predicted temperatures for your region and see how accurate the weather forecasters are. Do this for a week.

- Show the children what a maximum/minimum thermometer is. Again, record the temperature for a week and find the difference. This is interesting if done each season, as comparisons can be made.

- Use forehead fever scan thermometers to see what children's temperatures are. What happens when they go outside? Predict first!

Fractions

Finding halves and quarters of objects

We made a play dough dinner. We divided it into quarters. Each quarter should be exactly the same. Are they?

- Give each child a paper plate, and ask them to cut it into halves or quarters carefully. Make imitation food from playdough or Plasticine, and put identical food on each of the four sections, for example, two sausages, one egg, seven chips and nine peas. Reassemble the plates and talk about what the children can see **(see photograph above)**.

  Extension work could include pictures of incomplete plates where the children fill in the missing items.

N.B. The ideas below can be adapted for work on both halves and quarters

- Practise dividing a range of items into two equal pieces, for example, a length of string, jam tarts, apples, paper shapes, a glass of water, a lump of Plasticine, a tower of interlocking cubes. Talk about the equipment required to measure the accuracy of the sharing (or dividing), such as a set of balances to check the Plasticine.

- Fold a paper circle into quarters, cut out a 'snowflake' design and use this to make a screen print, or to produce rubbings.

- Make a range of goods, for example, sandwiches, mince pies, cakes from Plasticine, using biscuit and pastry cutters to get regular shapes. Practise cutting in half and putting the pieces on top of each other to check the accuracy of the cutting.

Finding halves and quarters of numbers

half & half

What did we do?

We used squares which were divided into 16 small squares, and we had to colour half black and leave half white.

We found that half of 16 is 8, so we started by colouring 8 squares in to make a pattern.

Then William thought of cutting each small square into 2, making 32 little triangles. Half of 32 is 16, so we found ways to colour 16 little triangles.

Jessica then drew lines to divide her squares into 32 rectangles, and she coloured 16 of those.

Last of all, Heather divided each of her squares into 4 triangles, making 64 triangles altogether. Half of 64 is 32, so we found ways to colour 32 of these tiny triangles. We did this again with tiny squares.

- Give each child a 4 x 4 piece of squared paper. Talk about how many small squares there are (16), and find half of that number (8). Ask the children to find as many different ways as they can to colour half of their piece of paper. Extend this by drawing lines to make the sixteen squares into smaller shapes such as 32 triangles, and now ask the children to find and colour a half **(see photograph above)**.

- **Introduce the idea of halves and quarters in a practical situation, by sharing out sweets, for example.** Show how many each child would get when eight sweets are shared between two children, and then four children. Repeat, using different totals of sweets, and get the children to record the results in picture format.

- Challenge a group of children to make a display of halves and quarters using classroom equipment such as Logipeople, Poleidoblocs, Lego, Clixi, pegs and boards, etc. **(see photograph above)**.

- As part of work on printing, get the children to produce "half and half" patterns, where they design and print a pattern of repeating shapes using stamps made from potato or sponge, using one colour for half their pattern and another colour for the rest of the pattern. For example, fold a sheet of paper in half four times to make sixteen sections. Use a potato shape to print eight red shapes in eight of the sections, and eight yellow shapes in the remaining sections. This can be extended by asking the children to produce designs where each quarter is a different colour.

- Similarly, paper weaving can be used to produce "half and half" patterns. Ask the children if they can make a paper weaving design where one quarter of the pattern is a different colour.

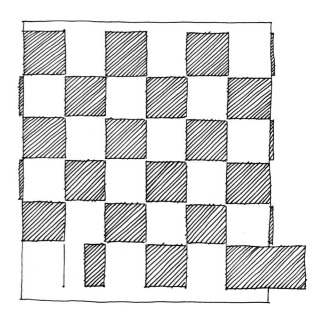

Take a number

- Cut a potato in the shape of a 0, and use it to print over a giant 0. Repeat with all the numbers to 9 **(see photograph)**.

- Ask the children to think of where they can see numbers at home. Make a display of children's drawings of numbers they have found at home.

- Train the children to use any appropriate classroom materials in their calculations, not just specific 'mathematical' apparatus. Initiate a discussion and make a list of items to help with number work, which may include pencils and crayons, rulers (number lines), Lego, Meccano and, of course, other children! Make sure everything is labelled and that children learn to find and put away items - this is practice in elementary sorting.

- Tell the children their number in the register and use this for number recognition, ordering, showing odd and even, counting in 2s, 5s, 10s. Try "Silly Maths", where Alison (number 5 in register), plus Madeleine (7) equals Iain (12). This also works for subtraction: Eleanor (19) take away Iain (12) equals Madeleine (7)!

- More discussion can arise from the many playground games that involve number, for example, "I'm a little bubble car", and "50/50". Talk to the children to find out which games are currently popular, and use these.

- Take a number each week and organise a display about that particular number. Include children's paintings, patterns and writing about the number, together with any investigative work. Make sure that the shape of the number can be clearly seen in different formats.

- You might begin this topic by discussing language and objects relating to numbers. Your list may include ideas such as:

  1 – noses, heads, unicycle, universe, unique, unicorn, unit, unite.
  2 – eyes, ears, twins, bicycle, binoculars, duet, duo, dual, double, duel, duplicate.
  3 – triangle, triplets, trio, tricycle, 'trice', tricolore, trident, trifoliate, triple, tripod.
  4 – wheels on vehicle, quarter, quadruplet, quadrangle, quadruped, quadruple, quart, quadrilateral.
  5 – fingers, quintuplets, quintuple, pentagon.
  6 – insect legs, sextuplets, sextuple, hexagon.
  7 – colours in the rainbow, sextuplets, septuple, September*, (also prefix *hepta-*).
  8 – octopus tentacles, spider legs, octave, octagon, octuple, October*.
  9 – nontuple, November* (Latin for ninth is *nonus*).
  10 – toes, decuple, December*, decimal.
  100 – century, centurion, centipede, centimetre.

- The ancient Roman first month had been March, prior to Julius and Augustus Caesar.

More/less than

- Children are always intrigued by the register, so use this fascination. For younger children, make a pictogram to show who is having a school dinner, who is having sandwiches, and who is going home. This will naturally give rise to "more than" and "less than" questions. (See illustration above.)

One-one matching

- Ask the children to collect items needed for their table. For example, "We need six pencils, six books, etc.".

Number lines

- Get the children to look at a computer keyboard and notice the different patterns.

- Give groups of children a theme, for example, "Rockets", and ask them to design and make a number line for the classroom.

Odds and evens/counting in 2s

- Write the numbers 1 to 10 on white cards. With the whole class present, give one of the cards (out of sequence) to a child and ask her/him to stand up and choose a group of children to equal the number on the card. Now ask if everyone in the group can find a partner. If they can't, the one without a partner must be the *odd* one out.

Write this number on the board in a set marked 'odd numbers'. Repeat with all the other numbers, collecting them into sets of odd or even numbers.

Now give the cards back to the children who were originally holding them, and ask them to identify their number as being odd or even. Ask them to get into sets, one odd, one even. Challenge them to order themselves, still in their odd or even set. Now replace their cards with coloured ones, say *red for even* and *green for odd*, and ask both sets to join and order themselves. What can the children see about the pattern of red and green cards?

- Investigate book page numbers.

Number stories

- Taking the numbers from 1 to 20, find something to say about each number, for example,
    "I have one cat"
    "I have lost two teeth"
    "There are three playgrounds in our school", etc.
  Record the results on a class chart, with each child contributing a picture and some writing.

Number line and 100 square activities

- Collect house numbers by asking the children where they live. Can they find their house number on the number line?

- Where would they live if they moved four houses along? or ten houses back? or at the house which is double their number?

Place value

- Ask the children to find out and write down their telephone numbers. Show them how to order these high numbers.

Addition and subtraction to 100

- Give each letter of the alphabet a number. Get the children to add up their name, using a calculator. Extend this by adding friends' names, and then ordering the class from lowest total to highest. See if any children share the same number.

- Ask the children to look at their television or video remote controls at home, and to copy the patterns on to squared paper. Compare these, and make a giant one for the wall. Look at how the numbers are set out.

  Try adding them across, vertically and diagonally - what happens? What happens when they add the different layouts?

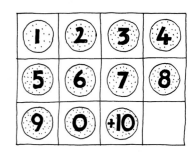

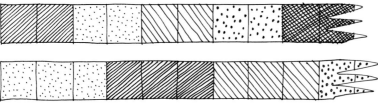

Multiplication and Division

- Using strips of squared paper with 20 squares, get the children to colour the first two using one colour, and then the next two in another colour. Continue until they reach the end of the strip. Were there any squares left over? Now try with a new strip, and colour blocks of three squares. What happens? Challenge the children to find out which numbers end exactly at 20 and which don't, and to record their findings.

Length

- Set the children work relating to body measurements (see chapter on Length, page 42).

Time

- Find everyone's birthday and order the class from oldest to youngest.
- Using the date of everyone's birthday, order the class - i.e. 2nd, 13th, 29th, etc.
- Find out which date is the most common, and display the results on a graph.
- Let the children work out challenges for each other based on calendars. For example, "What will the date be in three days, in three weeks, in three months?"
- Take the numbers of the year and re-order to make as many numbers as possible, for example, 1997, 1979, 1799, etc.
- Look at a clock and practise counting in 5s. Teach the children to play clock patience.

General investigations

- Bring in a collection of everyday items, for example, keys, stamps, shells, and discuss how to sort them - by colour, shape, size. Can they be sorted by weight, capacity or area?
- Ask every child in the class to choose their favourite number between 1 and 20 and record the results both in a standard format such as a block graph, and in the children's own chosen method.

Recording information

- Collect information about the children to record using different methods of pictorial representation. For example:
    - a Venn diagram showing the children with six letters in their name
    - a Carroll diagram to show children with and without brothers and sisters
    - block graphs or pictograms about family sizes.
  See the chapter "Pets" (page 66) and photograph in "Teddy Bears" (page 61) for other methods.

NUMBER THROUGH TOPIC

FOOD

> **NOTE:**
> When handling food with children, make them aware of safety aspects to do with hygiene, hot surfaces and sharp utensils.

Formation/recognition

- Make numbers from play dough, decorate and hang on the wall. Get the children to devise games using these numbers.

One to one matching

- Use the story of Goldilocks to match one-to-one.

Ordinal

- **Tell the story of "The Gingerbread Man"**, where the gingerbread man was chased by the little old man and the little old lady, etc. Get the children to make Plasticine or clay models of the characters and have cards with 1st, 2nd, 3rd to match to the characters. Set up the story, including the river - this could include a quartered gingerbread man at the end! Another suitable story for this activity would be "The Enormous Turnip". **(See photograph above.)**

Money

- Tell the story of "The Elephant and the Bad Baby", and set up a food stall with buns costing 1p, crisps costing 2p, etc.

Base Work

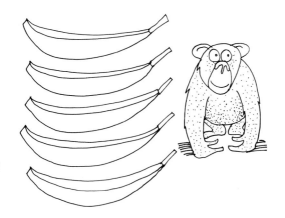

- Make up appropriate games based on exchanging. Ideas could include:
    ### Base 5 - "Going Bananas!"
    Collect five bananas, exchange for a bunch, exchange five bunches for a tree - or a monkey.
    ### Base 6 - "All the Fun of the Fair!"
    Collect six coconuts, exchange for a picture of a shy with six coconuts in it, exchange six shies to win a teddy bear.

Bonds to 10

Play "Choccies".
For two players you will need:
    six bars of chocolate, cut out of card and partitioned into ten sections. Make one complete bar, and cut up the five others to make each of the following pairs:
        1+9 2+8 3+7 4+6 5+5
    a baseboard with the outline shape of each pair.

To play:
Share the pieces randomly between two children, who take turns to match them back on to the board. Every time they complete a number bond, they win a point. The child with the most points wins.

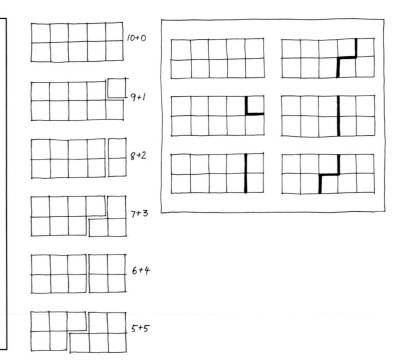

Ordering 10 - 20 and Place value

- Cut up a melon and estimate the number of seeds. Ask the children to come up with ideas about how to make this easier, and someone will realise that ten is a good number to count in. When seeds are washed, stick them on to card in sets of ten and use for counting.

Play "Number Stew".
For two players, you will need:
    a selection of magnetic numbers (fridge magnets)
    a large bowl to serve as the "cooking pot"

To play:
Put the magnetic numbers in the pot and let the children take turns to fish them out with
magnets and then arrange them to make the largest number/smallest number.

- **Make an alternative "Healthy Eating" Hansel and Gretel house** with pasta decoration on the door, and fruit and vegetable paintings on the roof and walls. Use this as a stimulus for counting, measuring, and for estimation.

Money to £1+

- Investigate value for money in multipacks of sweets.

- With the help of parents, have a trip to a local shop to buy food for a class picnic. Before you go, work out quantities needed. For example, if each child would like half an apple, and there are 28 children in the class, how many apples will we need? If apples cost 5p each, how much will it all cost? How many bottles of juice (loaves of bread, etc.) will be needed?

- Do some cooking, and set up a classroom café. Pizzas are simple, and offer a wide choice of flavours. Invite the parents to come and buy the food. How many items will be needed? What flavours should be made? (Make block graphs to show the children's suggestions.) How much will it cost altogether? How much will the children sell each whole pizza for? How much would half a pizza cost? This will involve costing ingredients, cooking times, weighing, etc.

Angles

- Cut a pizza (real or pretend) into quarters to show the right angles produced. Then cut another into sixths and look at the angles - are they larger or smaller? Try with pieces of other sizes.

Fractions

- Make a range of play food from Plasticine or play dough. Use these to investigate fractions. Make 'sponge' cakes to cut into halves and quarters (pointing out the right angles when cutting into quarters).

  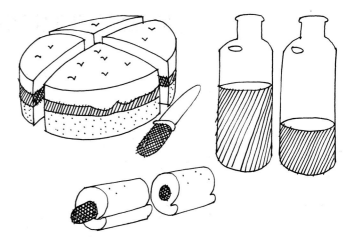

  Use little plastic drinks bottles to half and quarter fill with 'raspberry juice' (water with food colouring added).

  'Sausage rolls' can be halved by cutting and balancing on scales.

- Play dough 'sweets' can be shared between children to find halves and quarters.

Weight, Area and Length

- Weigh a slice of bread and draw round it with a coloured pen on a piece of paper. Leave the slice out for several days. Weigh it daily, and draw round in a different coloured felt-tip pen each day to show shrinkage of area. The area can be found by drawing round the slice on centimetre squared paper. Ask the children why the bread loses weight and becomes smaller.

- Peel an apple and measure the length of the skin.

- Spread the apple skin out on centimetre squared paper and count how many squares it covers.

Time

- Discuss cooking times and the temperature of ovens, if appropriate.

- **Make sand timers from little plastic bottles.**

Data Handling

- Ask the children about their favourite foods, and record the results.

- Divide the class into groups and ask each group to gather the same information, such as "How do you like to eat your eggs?" Ensure that each group presents the results in a different format, for example, by mapping, Carroll diagram, Venn diagram, trackway, block graph.

- Send groups of children on a whole school survey about Healthy Eating. Once the data is collected and has been recorded in the chosen format, each group should think up a number of questions for the other groups to answer using the information presented.

Logic/Algebra

- Explore repeating patterns on crockery.

- Make pasta necklaces by dyeing dried pasta with food colouring and then threading these on to string.

- Print repeating patterns using fruit and vegetables.

- Let the children explore seating plans at lunchtime. For example: How many children can be seated at eight tables if six sit at each?

NUMBER THROUGH TOPIC

TEDDY BEARS

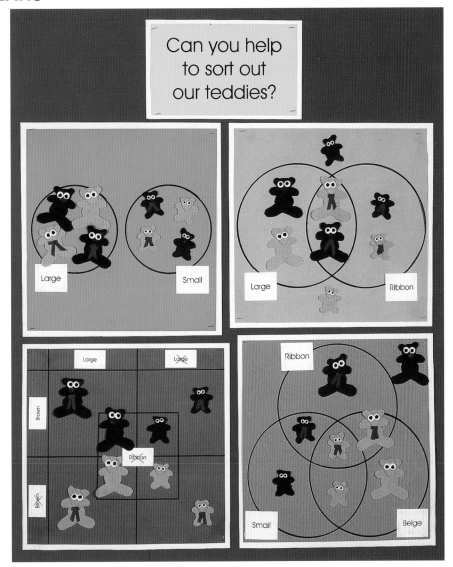

See Sorting below

This topic allows many opportunities for work on measure. Ask the children to bring in their bears. With luck, you should get a wide range with which to try out the following suggestions. Although initial discussions should involve the whole class, the activities are best done in groups to begin with, as comparisons with fewer items are more manageable for the children.

Sorting
- Let the children choose the categories to begin with. They may choose colour or size, but with encouragement will become more discriminating and begin to differentiate further, choosing criteria such as texture of fur, age of teddy, clothes worn or not, cuddliness, type of fabric, etc. **(See photograph above.)**

Measuring
- Initiate discussion as to what to measure before starting. Some children may need to use non-standard units, whereas others will be ready to use centimetres and grammes.

Length
- The children may want to begin with height and will simply order the bears. This can evolve into comparing Multilink towers made to match the heights of the bears, or measurements made with rulers. Again, important discussions will arise as to where exactly to begin and end the measuring (top of head, or top of ears?), thus leading to an understanding of the need for standardising measurements.

- Other measurements could include the length of arms, legs and ears. Ask the children how they can find out how fat their teddy is. Depending on the development of the children, they may use string, or tape measures. Ask them to think of other places to measure - they should suggest necks, wrists and legs. To record this information, give them a teddy-shaped book, with places to measure already drawn in. An extension of this work would be to measure their own wrists, waists, etc., and find the difference.

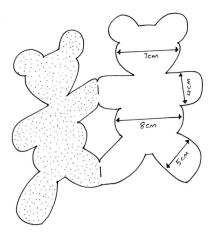

- Once all the bears on the table have been measured, ask the children to put them in order. Again, they will need to decide what to order - height? fattest to thinnest? When they have managed this, ask the children to tie a label round each bear showing the chosen measurement, for example, height. Combine two groups of children and ask them to order the bears now. Eventually, ask the whole class to order their bears - quite an achievement!

- Make Teddy Sums. Using the children's teddy bears brought from home, measure each using Multibase cubes (each of which is 1cm). Then ask the children to use this information to find two teddies which, when standing one on top of the other, are the same height as a third teddy. Get them to check using the teddies.

Weight

- Ask the groups how they will find which is the heaviest bear on the table. Get them to estimate first. For some children, comparison by balance will be sufficient, but others will be able to go on to use grammes and kilogrammes. Once this is done, the same process as used with length can be followed.

- Once the whole class has ordered their bears, interesting facts may be discovered. Can the children find two little bears that weigh the same as a big one? Whose is the heaviest? the lightest? What is the difference between them? Is there a bear that weighs the amount of the difference? Arrange a display to show this.

- An extension activity of the above would be to ask two children to work together and compare their bears' measurements, involving finding the difference(s).

- Ask the children to: - find a bear weighing twice theirs
  - find a bear who is half the weight of theirs
  - find something in the classroom which weighs the same as their bear, and make a display of several bears and the objects which weigh the same, and see if the children can match them
  - find the total weight of all the bears in the class.

- Get the children to draw their bears on to a card and write on it the weight in grammes. The cards can then be used to perform operations without needing the bears present. For example, adding the weight of three bears (this may involve exchanging kilogrammes if several bears are quite large); subtracting the weight of one bear from another; taking a handful of cards at random and ordering the weights, etc.

- Show the children how to use scales with a dial. Make a giant size dial to show the gradations, add a pointer and get the children to show on this how much their teddy weighs. Ask them to bring in kitchen scales from home to ensure a variety of dials, and let them weigh each other's teddies.

Area

- Get the children to draw around their teddy to find its area. Again, ask the children to estimate first - both how many squares their teddy will cover, and whose will cover the most. Discuss what they will do with bits of squares.

Data handling

- Once the above information has been gathered, the way is open to displaying it using a range of graphs and diagrams. The level of sophistication is again dependent upon the abilities of the class. If the children have had experience of data handling activities, ask them to think what type of graph would best show information of, perhaps, the height of teddies in a group; or, perhaps you want to know if the bigger teddies are the heaviest. What sort of diagram would show this? Encourage the children to work independently of you, both in choosing the type of graph, collecting, collating and displaying the information, and for thinking up questions for others to interpret.

1 to 20 Addition/subtraction game

Play "Teddy Bears' Picnic" game.
For up to four players, you will need:
      a base board (see drawing) - six of the numbers on each path need to be coloured, each in a different colour.
      Marker cards (one for each player) made by the children (by drawing a teddy on card - coloured, cut out, and held upright by a piece of adhesive putty or Plasticine)
      Three spinners - one four-sided and marked with + and - , the other two each with six sides, marked 0,1,2,3,4,5 and 5,6,7,8,9,10.
      A standard die.

To play:
The teddies start from Home, and advance towards the picnic by throwing the die. If a teddy lands on a coloured stone, the player must spin all three spinners and perform the appropriate calculation. If the sum is correct, s/he may throw the dice again and move that number of steps. If the sum is wrong, s/he stays where s/he is. The winner is the first teddy to go to the picnic and get home again.

Variations could include each child having two teddies to get to the picnic and home again, or varying the mathematical calculations required when landing on a coloured stone.

NUMBER THROUGH TOPIC

CLOTHES

General

- Use clothes for counting in:
  - 1s - hats, scarves
  - 5s - gloves
  - 2s - gloves, shoes, socks
  - 10s - pairs of gloves.

  Other countables might be eyelets in shoes, pockets and buttons. Look closely at a patterned jumper and transfer the pattern on to squared paper.

Shoes

- Make rubbings of sole patterns and try transferring the pattern on to squared or triangular paper. Colourwash over the wax sole rubbings and ask children to match the pairs. Make it harder by washing each sole a different colour.

- Discuss shoe sizing and explain the way in which children's shoes go by 11, 12, 13, 1, 2, 3. To illustrate this clearly, find an example of each and display on a grid, thus showing the increase in size. Include half-sizes.

- **Make a Shoe Tree (see photograph on facing page).** Select a branch, making sure that there are enough twigs for the range of shoe sizes in your class. If you cannot find a suitable branch, make a construction from chicken wire and papier mâché. Insert this into a clay pot filled with gravel and label each twig with a shoe size. Get the children to make sole rubbings of their shoes using wax crayon, cut these out and mount on to card. Attach these to the correct branch using paperclips. Under the tree, you could make a line of cut-out rubbings, in order of size, and labelled so that the children can see the increasing size. Talk about the shoe sizing system, where size 1 is after size 13.

- Measure the shoes from heel to toe and find the longest. **Get the children to measure their parents' shoes and then order them.** Does the tallest person in the class have the biggest feet? Does the shortest have the smallest feet?

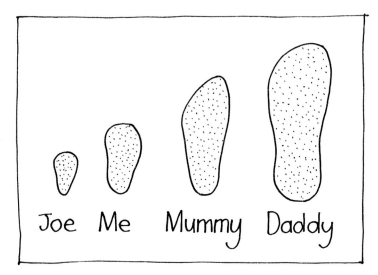

- Show the types of shoe fastenings found in the class using various formats of pictorial representation. Include a chart showing who has learnt to tie their laces!

- Compare lengths of laces. Ask the children to estimate how long their laces are, then measure them. Look at the different ways to lace shoes.

- Investigate shoe boxes. Go to a shoe shop and ask them to collect boxes until you have enough for all the children to have one. The boxes can be measured, explored for right angles, filled with cubes, etc. When all activities have been exhausted, the outsides can be decorated in a suitably mathematical fashion, and the interiors turned into miniature peephole theatres.

Button Maths

- Send out a school-wide appeal for unwanted buttons to build up a huge range.

- Give each group a selection of buttons and ask them to find ways in which to sort them. Get them to display their sorting by attaching their buttons on to card (using adhesive putty), and then challenge the rest of the class to guess how each group has sorted.

See Shoe Tree on facing page

- Give each child a handful of buttons and ask them how many different things they can find out about them. They may order by size, pair them up to find if they have an odd and even amount, sort by how many holes each has, use their buttons to explore halves and quarters of amounts, etc.

- Use buttons with two holes for counting in 2s, likewise buttons with four holes. Let them try problem-solving: "If I have three buttons with four holes in each, how many holes would that be?" Ask them to make up their own questions to ask other children.
  Similarly, encourage division problems: "If I have two shirts and ten buttons to sew on to them, how many buttons will each shirt have?"

- **Ribbons**
  Buy an assortment and let the children order by length and width. Let them estimate how long each piece is, then measure to find out. They can then explore the classroom for things which are longer or shorter, wider or narrower than their own ribbon. Ask the children to estimate which ribbons, when laid end to end, will be shorter/longer or about the same as a metre. If pieces are cut into 50cm and 25cm lengths, you could go on to investigate fractions. The children will quickly discover that ribbons are good for measuring around things too, which will lead to more estimating and checking.

NUMBER THROUGH TOPIC

PETS

Because this topic provides many opportunities for working with data, the children can gain valuable experience of working with pictorial representation and sorting activities.

As well as producing their own diagrams, children need practice in 'reading' and interpreting graphs and tables which have been produced by others. Encourage them to ask and answer questions about charts and diagrams.

When recording information, it is important that children have the chance to record the same data in a variety of ways. Hearing the same answers to questions such as "How many children have a pet rabbit?" when applied to different types of pictorial representation, will help them to develop conservation of number.

- Get the children to each produce several small drawings of themselves with their name written clearly underneath. Cover these with clear plastic, and use when carrying out sorting activities or producing a chart. In addition to this, make a set of cards with drawings of the pets owned by the children in the class, together with the negative version ("cat" and "no cat", which would be a drawing of a cat with a cross through it) to be used in the same way.

Pictorial Representations

- These methods of presenting information in a visual form involve one-to-one correspondence and comparison between sets. Questions which could be applied to all the methods should relate to understanding, counting and comparison:

  What can you tell me about the children in this row/column/set?
  Which pet do six children have?
  How many children have a gerbil?
  Are there more children with dogs or with goldfish?
  How many more?
  Which pet is the most/least popular?

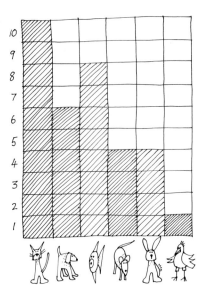

- Ask the children to put the pets into order of popularity. Can they find whether two-legged pets are more popular than four-legged pets?

- Write animal sums which can be answered by referring to the charts:
  Horses + cats =
  Dogs - hamsters =

Pictograms

Each child sticks a picture of himself in the correct position. If the children write their names on the pictures, answers to questions such as, "How many pets does Kareem have?" can be found.

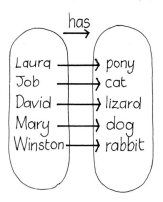

Mapping

The children draw arrows from their name to the pet they own, or from the type of pet to the kind of skin which the pet has.

We made a block graph about our pets.

mice | fish | hamsters | gerbils | dogs | geese | cats | snakes

Block Graphs

- These can be horizontal or vertical, and are more abstract than pictograms. The children colour in individual blocks rather than use pictures. Try making 3D versions! **(See photograph.)**

Venn Diagrams

- Sets are made from children fulfilling the required characteristic, for example, "the set of children who have cats". Draw large Venn or Carroll diagrams on the playground in chalk when talking about sorting the children in the class into groups according to various criteria, and get the children to place themselves in the correct set. Always draw attention to the children who are not in the set and ask why, and include the idea of an empty set.

- Children can be introduced to more advanced diagrams which involve intersections.

• Carroll Diagram

Can you tell me how many children have a cat and a dog?
Who has a cat but not a dog?
What can you tell me about the pets Sophia has?

• Number Operations

Tails, ears and paws all give opportunities for repeated addition and multiplication: How many ears on all the rabbits belonging to children in the class? How many tails? How many beaks? How many cats and fish are there? How many legs are there altogether on the two-legged animals?

	cat	c̶a̶t̶
dog	Alex Jonah Natasha	Sophia
d̶o̶g̶	Alison Jason	Ben

MATHS TRAILS

A Maths Trail is an organised walk through an area close to the school, where the children can experience mathematical ideas in the real world.

If it is true that children learn through activities which relate directly to their own experiences, then a Maths Trail set in a known environment is an ideal learning situation. It takes advantage of their natural curiosity and sense of enquiry, helps them to view the familiar through new eyes, and hopefully teaches them to respect and appreciate their environment.

Setting up a Maths Trail

Maths Trails generally consist of seven or eight "activity sites", where children stop and work. Sometimes the grounds of a school provide sufficient sites, whereas in other places, the trail spreads into the local environment. There is usually a set of worksheets, ideally collated into a booklet, which the children work through over a period of time. Some sites will need to be revisited throughout the school year: for example, where the height of a plant is to be measured as it grows.

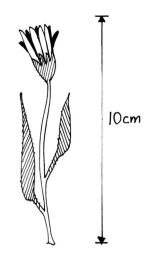

Within the groups of most schools, there should be opportunities for the children to study:

Shape -   windows and doors
              brick patterns
              paving slab patterns
              roofing tiles
              climbing frames
              right angles
              symmetry

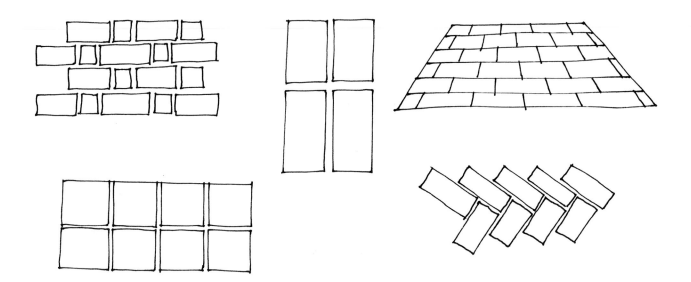

Number –	counting steps and stairs
	measuring distances
	measuring plant growth
	repeating patterns
	estimation
	timing activities
	sorting and classifying, for example, leaves, seeds and fruits
	co-ordinates on a map of the trail.

Data handling –	graph making
	weather recording
	interviews and questionnaires
	tallying, for example, the number of birds visiting the bird table.

Within the local environment, there are likely to be facilities which could enrich the Maths Trail. (When taking the children out of the school grounds, ensure that you have sufficient adults accompanying you, and that the children are very clear about how to behave, before leaving the classroom.)

Places to visit may include:

On the road –	traffic and pedestrian surveys
	shapes of road signs
	distances on signposts
	house numbers
	car number plates

Churches –	2D and 3D shape
	dates on gravestones, for example, "Who, of the people buried here, had lived the longest?"
	fees for weddings, etc.
	symmetry
	number of places along a pew/pews, in a row/rows in the church
	number and shape of panes in stained glass windows
	dates and times of services.

Shops –	opening times
	survey of numbers of shoppers at certain times
	money handling, including giving change
	range of products, for example, "How many types of cheese are there?"
	cost of basic food items
	meaning of words such as "Best Buy", "On Offer", "Economy size".

Post Office –	collection times
	measuring a pillar box (height, girth, size of slot)
	price of stamps
	weight of parcels

Recording Work

Observations and discussions should be recorded in a manner which matches the needs of the children.
Suggestions could include:

completing a pre-written booklet   making collections
the use of a tape recorder   taking photographs or making a video film
drawings   rubbings
graphs   questionnaires
writing   artwork

The Booklets

These should include a clear map of the complete Maths Trail, with the activity sites marked. It may also be necessary to include enlarged maps of individual sites.

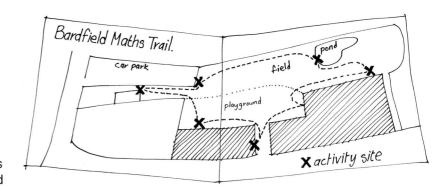

A code which tells the children which activities are to be carried out "on site", and which need to be done back in the classroom, avoids time-consuming tasks being carried out under unsuitable conditions.

As children of different ages and abilities will be using the Maths Trail, it may be worth considering writing a couple of booklets aimed at different ability levels. Older children could be involved in writing material for younger children.

The booklet should include a wide range of types of tasks, such as drawing, counting, calculating, writing answers and ticking boxes in response to questions. Activities such as model-making and finished artwork would be done back in the classroom.

Ideas for Playground Markings

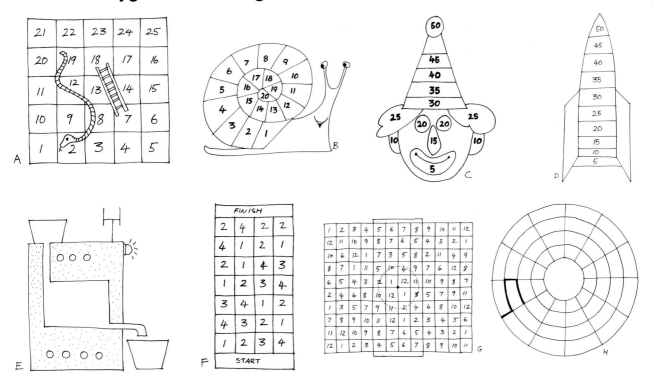

Playground markings can provide a stimulus for the children to make up their own games, and can also act as a focus for teacher-led activities. When dice are required, each player could use their own individual one, or the large, foam versions could be used.

Suggestions include:

A   Traditional board games

B   Snail number line

C   Clown face for target practice

D   Rocket number line, counting in 5s

E   Function machine

F   Racetrack: the children can make up their own games on this, perhaps using a die.

G   Games can be invented on this base. One suggestion might be "Football".
A skittle, representing the ball, is placed on the centre spot. The aim is to carry the skittle into your opponent's goal. The players stand on a square along their rear line, and take turns to throw a die. Players subtract their score from the number of the square they are standing on (or vice versa, depending which is the larger number). They then choose which squares to move to. The first player to reach an adjacent square to the skittle can pick it up, and then carry it, on their next move, towards the opponent's goad. To capture the skittle from that player, opponents have to land on the same square and thus take possession, sending the dispossessed player back to their rear line. Players cannot under any other circumstances, land on the same square as another player. It is a game of attack and defence, through blocking the pathway to the goals.

H   "Knock Out". The players choose their own starting position on any of the intersections along the outer edge. They take turns to throw a die, and move along the lines for the corresponding number of intersections, turning corners or travelling in straight lines as they choose. The object of the game is to "land" on an opponent. When this happens, the opponent is sent to the centre, where they have to throw a 6 to re-enter the game.

For details of further Belair publications
please write to:

BELAIR PUBLICATIONS LTD.
P.O. Box 12, TWICKENHAM, TW1 2QL, England

For sales and distribution (outside USA and Canada)
FOLENS PUBLISHERS
Albert House, Apex Business Centre
Boscombe Road, DUNSTABLE, Bedfordshire, LU5 4RL
England